The Open University

M208 Pure

CW00546929

LA3

Vector spaces

This publication forms part of an Open University course. Details of this and other Open University courses can be obtained from the Student Registration and Enquiry Service, The Open University, PO Box 197, Milton Keynes, MK7 6BJ, United Kingdom: tel. +44 (0)870 300 6090, e-mail general-enquiries@open.ac.uk

Alternatively, you may visit the Open University website at http://www.open.ac.uk where you can learn more about the wide range of courses and packs offered at all levels by The Open University.

To purchase a selection of Open University course materials, visit http://www.ouw.co.uk, or contact Open University Worldwide, Michael Young Building, Walton Hall, Milton Keynes, MK7 6AA, United Kingdom, for a brochure: tel. +44 (0)1908 858793, fax +44 (0)1908 858787, e-mail ouw-customer-services@open.ac.uk

The Open University, Walton Hall, Milton Keynes, MK7 6AA.

First published 2006. Reprinted with amendments 2007.

Edited, designed and typeset by The Open University, using the Open University TeX System.

Printed and bound in the United Kingdom by Hobbs the Printers Limited, Brunel Road, Totton, Hampshire SO40 3WX.

ISBN 0 7492 0224 6

1.2

Contents

Introduction

In this unit we introduce a mathematical structure which is one of the most important unifying concepts of pure mathematics, that of a *vector space*. This consists of a set of elements called *vectors*, which need not be geometric vectors, and two operations, *addition of vectors* and *multiplication by a scalar*. You have already met two vector spaces briefly, $\mathbb{R}^2$ and $\mathbb{R}^3$, but so far we have made no attempt to look systematically at their properties.

Unit LA1, Section 2.

Section 1 starts with $\mathbb{R}^2$ and $\mathbb{R}^3$, and looks at the properties shared by these spaces and others. This leads to n-dimensional space $\mathbb{R}^n$ and to the formal definition of a vector space. We then show how to test whether a given set is a vector space, and look at a wide range of examples of vector spaces.

In Section 2 we show you how to combine vectors in a vector space. We introduce the idea of a *linear combination* of vectors, and look at the vectors that result from taking all possible linear combinations of a given set of vectors; we call this the *span* of the vectors. Where it is possible, we look at this span geometrically.

In Section 3 we consider minimal sets of vectors that span a particular vector space. Any such set is called a *basis* for the vector space. In order to find such sets, we introduce two other ideas, *linear independence* and *linear dependence*. We discover that every basis is a linearly independent set of vectors that spans the vector space. If a vector space has a finite basis, then every basis contains the same number of vectors. We call this number the *dimension* of the vector space; otherwise, we say that the vector space is infinite dimensional. We see that, when the vector space is a geometric space such as $\mathbb{R}^2$ and $\mathbb{R}^3$, this definition of dimension agrees with our geometric ideas of dimension.

Section 4 introduces the idea of a *subspace* of a vector space as a subset of a vector space which is itself a vector space; this is similar to the relationship between subgroups and groups. Where possible, we look at subspaces both algebraically and geometrically, and we find bases for subspaces of various vector spaces.

In Section 5 we return to bases, and restrict ourselves to $\mathbb{R}^n$. We define an *orthogonal basis* as one for which the vectors are all orthogonal to each other. Orthogonal bases are useful because they arise frequently in geometric situations. It is particularly easy to represent a vector as a linear combination of the vectors in an orthogonal basis.

Study guide

Sections 1–5 should be studied in the natural order.

Sections 1–4 contain the main ideas in the unit, and will form the bulk of your study. They contain quite a few theorems and proofs. You will not be asked to reproduce any of these proofs, but we hope that you will read them and try to understand their structure. Section 3 is the longest of these sections.

Section 5 contains the audio section.

1   Vector spaces

After working through this section, you should be able to:

(a) understand the definition of a *real vector space*;

(b) check whether a given set of elements forms a vector space under the operations of vector addition and scalar multiplication.

1.1 Euclidean spaces

In Unit LA1 you met the Euclidean spaces $\mathbb{R}^2$ and $\mathbb{R}^3$. The elements of $\mathbb{R}^2$ are vectors (x, y) with two components with respect to a given pair of axes. The elements of $\mathbb{R}^3$ are vectors (x, y, z) with three components. You also met two operations, addition of vectors and multiplication of a vector by a scalar. In that unit we defined these two operations on $\mathbb{R}^2$ and $\mathbb{R}^3$ as follows.

Definitions In $\mathbb{R}^2$, the set of ordered pairs of real numbers, the operations of **addition** and of **multiplication by a scalar** are defined as:

$$(u_1, u_2) + (v_1, v_2) = (u_1 + v_1, u_2 + v_2),$$

$$\alpha(u_1, u_2) = (\alpha u_1, \alpha u_2), \quad \text{where } \alpha \in \mathbb{R}.$$

In $\mathbb{R}^3$, the set of ordered triples of real numbers, the operations of **addition** and of **multiplication by a scalar** are defined as:

$$(u_1, u_2, u_3) + (v_1, v_2, v_3) = (u_1 + v_1, u_2 + v_2, u_3 + v_3),$$

$$\alpha(u_1, u_2, u_3) = (\alpha u_1, \alpha u_2, \alpha u_3), \quad \text{where } \alpha \in \mathbb{R}.$$

We also stated that $\mathbb{R}^2$ and $\mathbb{R}^3$ are vector spaces. They are particular instances of a class of mathematical structures called vector spaces. In this unit we look at many other examples, at the properties that are common to all of them, and at how they can be used.

We concentrate first on vectors in $\mathbb{R}^2$ and $\mathbb{R}^3$, as these are vectors with which you are familiar, but there is no reason to stop at $\mathbb{R}^3$—why not $\mathbb{R}^4$, $\mathbb{R}^5$, or even $\mathbb{R}^n$, for larger positive integers n?

Although it is impossible to visualise vectors in spaces with dimension greater than three, we can carry out exactly the same algebraic manipulations with these vectors, and these spaces are also vector spaces.

We now define exactly what we mean by $\mathbb{R}^n$.

Definition If n is a positive integer, then an **ordered n-tuple** is a sequence of real numbers $(u_1, u_2, \ldots, u_n)$. The set of all ordered n-tuples is called **n-dimensional space**, and is denoted by $\mathbb{R}^n$.

Vector addition and scalar multiplication are defined as in $\mathbb{R}^2$ and $\mathbb{R}^3$.

If $\mathbf{u} = (u_1, u_2, \ldots, u_n)$ and $\mathbf{v} = (v_1, v_2, \ldots, v_n)$ belong to $\mathbb{R}^n$, then

$$\begin{aligned}
\mathbf{u} + \mathbf{v} &= (u_1, u_2, \ldots, u_n) + (v_1, v_2, \ldots, v_n) \\
&= (u_1 + v_1, u_2 + v_2, \ldots, u_n + v_n)
\end{aligned}$$

and, for $\alpha \in \mathbb{R}$,

$$\alpha \mathbf{u} = (\alpha u_1, \alpha u_2, \ldots, \alpha u_n).$$

Example 1.1   In $\mathbb{R}^n$, let $\mathbf{u} = (1, 1, \ldots, 1)$ and $\mathbf{v} = (1, 2, \ldots, n)$. Form the vectors $\mathbf{u} + \mathbf{v}$ and $2\mathbf{u}$.

Solution $\mathbf{u} + \mathbf{v} = (1, 1, \ldots, 1) + (1, 2, \ldots, n) = (2, 3, \ldots, n + 1)$,

$2\mathbf{u} = 2(1, 1, \ldots, 1) = (2, 2, \ldots, 2)$.   ■

> **Exercise 1.1**   In $\mathbb{R}^5$, let $\mathbf{u} = (1, -1, 2, 0, -3)$ and $\mathbf{v} = (0, 2, -1, 4, 0)$. Form the vectors $\mathbf{u} + \mathbf{v}$ and $-3\mathbf{u}$.

This method of proceeding is common throughout mathematics. We start with spaces like $\mathbb{R}^2$ and $\mathbb{R}^3$ which we can visualise, we look at their properties, and then we generalise these properties to spaces that we cannot visualise, such as $\mathbb{R}^n$. We go from particular cases to a general case.

We can go even further, and think of a vector with a never-ending list of components $(v_1, v_2, v_3, \ldots)$. This is hard to visualise, but is not difficult to handle mathematically. The set of such vectors is called $\mathbb{R}^\infty$, and is an infinite-dimensional vector space. Vector addition and scalar multiplication are again performed component-wise.

We define the *dimension* of a vector space in Section 3.

Example 1.2   In $\mathbb{R}^\infty$, let $\mathbf{u} = (1, 0, 1, 0, 1, \ldots)$ and $\mathbf{v} = (1, -2, 3, -4, 5, \ldots)$. Form the vectors $\mathbf{u} + \mathbf{v}$ and $5\mathbf{u}$.

Solution $\mathbf{u} + \mathbf{v} = (1, 0, 1, 0, 1, \ldots) + (1, -2, 3, -4, 5, \ldots)$
$= (2, -2, 4, -4, 6, \ldots)$,

$5\mathbf{u} = 5(1, 0, 1, 0, 1, \ldots) = (5, 0, 5, 0, 5, \ldots)$.   ■

1.2 Real vector spaces

In the previous subsection we observed that $\mathbb{R}^n$ is a vector space for each n, but we did not give the definition of a vector space. Before giving the definition, we look at $\mathbb{R}^4$ and a set of polynomials, and show that, despite their apparent differences, these sets share many important properties.

A vector in $\mathbb{R}^4$ has the form (v_1, v_2, v_3, v_4), where v_1, v_2, v_3 and v_4 are real numbers, and the operations of vector addition and scalar multiplication are as defined in the previous subsection.

If we have two vectors $\mathbf{u} = (u_1, u_2, u_3, u_4)$ and $\mathbf{v} = (v_1, v_2, v_3, v_4)$ in $\mathbb{R}^4$, then their sum is also in $\mathbb{R}^4$ because

$$\begin{aligned}
\mathbf{u} + \mathbf{v} &= (u_1, u_2, u_3, u_4) + (v_1, v_2, v_3, v_4) \\
&= (u_1 + v_1, u_2 + v_2, u_3 + v_3, u_4 + v_4).
\end{aligned}$$

This last vector also belongs to $\mathbb{R}^4$ because each of the four coordinates is a real number, and so $\mathbb{R}^4$ is *closed under vector addition*.

For example, if $\mathbf{u} = (1, 3, 5, 7)$ and $\mathbf{v} = (2, -1, -5, 6)$ are vectors in $\mathbb{R}^4$, then

$$\mathbf{u} + \mathbf{v} = (1, 3, 5, 7) + (2, -1, -5, 6) = (3, 2, 0, 13),$$

which is a vector in $\mathbb{R}^4$.

We ask you to verify some other properties involving vector addition in the next exercise.

Exercise 1.2   In $\mathbb{R}^4$, let $\mathbf{u} = (u_1, u_2, u_3, u_4)$, $\mathbf{v} = (v_1, v_2, v_3, v_4)$ and $\mathbf{w} = (w_1, w_2, w_3, w_4)$. Verify that the following general results hold.

(a) $\mathbf{u} + \mathbf{v} = \mathbf{v} + \mathbf{u}$ *(a) is the commutative law.*

(b) $(\mathbf{u} + \mathbf{v}) + \mathbf{w} = \mathbf{u} + (\mathbf{v} + \mathbf{w})$ *(b) is the associative law.*

(c) $\mathbf{v} + \mathbf{0} = \mathbf{0} + \mathbf{v} = \mathbf{v}$, where $\mathbf{0}$ is the zero vector $(0, 0, 0, 0)$.

(d) $\mathbf{v} + (-\mathbf{v}) = \mathbf{0}$, where $-\mathbf{v} = (-v_1, -v_2, -v_3, -v_4)$.

We have now seen that, under vector addition, $\mathbb{R}^4$ satisfies the four group axioms

G1 CLOSURE,   G2 IDENTITY,   G3 INVERSES,   G4 ASSOCIATIVITY,

so $\mathbb{R}^4$ is a group under vector addition, with the zero vector $(0, 0, 0, 0)$ as the identity, and $-\mathbf{v}$ as the inverse of $\mathbf{v}$.

Note that, by Exercise 1.2(a), $\mathbb{R}^4$ is an Abelian group.

These properties all involve vector addition, but $\mathbb{R}^4$ also has some properties that involve scalar multiplication.

Let $\mathbf{v} = (v_1, v_2, v_3, v_4) \in \mathbb{R}^4$ and $\alpha \in \mathbb{R}$. Then

$$\alpha\mathbf{v} = \alpha(v_1, v_2, v_3, v_4) = (\alpha v_1, \alpha v_2, \alpha v_3, \alpha v_4).$$

This vector also belongs to $\mathbb{R}^4$, so $\mathbb{R}^4$ is *closed under scalar multiplication*.

For example, if $\mathbf{v} = (1, 2, -5, -3) \in \mathbb{R}^4$ and $\alpha = 4$, then

$$\alpha\mathbf{v} = 4(1, 2, -5, -3) = (4, 8, -20, -12),$$

which belongs to $\mathbb{R}^4$.

Note that if you multiply a vector in $\mathbb{R}^4$ by β, and then by α, you obtain the same result as multiplying by $\alpha\beta$. This is because, for all $\alpha, \beta \in \mathbb{R}$ and $\mathbf{v} = (v_1, v_2, v_3, v_4) \in \mathbb{R}^4$,

$$\begin{aligned}
\alpha(\beta\mathbf{v}) &= \alpha(\beta(v_1, v_2, v_3, v_4)) \\
&= \alpha(\beta v_1, \beta v_2, \beta v_3, \beta v_4) \\
&= (\alpha\beta v_1, \alpha\beta v_2, \alpha\beta v_3, \alpha\beta v_4) \\
&= (\alpha\beta)(v_1, v_2, v_3, v_4) \\
&= (\alpha\beta)\mathbf{v}.
\end{aligned}$$

For example, if $\mathbf{v} = (1, 2, -5, -3) \in \mathbb{R}^4$ and $\alpha = 4$, $\beta = -2$, then

$$\begin{aligned}
\alpha(\beta\mathbf{v}) &= 4(-2(1, 2, -5, -3)) \\
&= 4(-2, -4, 10, 6) \\
&= (-8, -16, 40, 24) \\
&= (-8)(1, 2, -5, -3) \\
&= (\alpha\beta)\mathbf{v}.
\end{aligned}$$

Also, if $\mathbf{v} = (v_1, v_2, v_3, v_4)$, then

$$1\mathbf{v} = 1(v_1, v_2, v_3, v_4) = (v_1, v_2, v_3, v_4) = \mathbf{v}.$$

Finally, there are two properties that connect vector addition and scalar multiplication:

$$\alpha(\mathbf{u} + \mathbf{v}) = \alpha\mathbf{u} + \alpha\mathbf{v},$$

$$(\alpha + \beta)\mathbf{v} = \alpha\mathbf{v} + \beta\mathbf{v}.$$

These are the distributive laws.

For example, if $\mathbf{u} = (1, 3, 5, 7)$ and $\mathbf{v} = (2, -1, -5, 6)$ are vectors in $\mathbb{R}^4$, and $\alpha = 3$ and $\beta = 4$, then

$$3((1, 3, 5, 7) + (2, -1, -5, 6)) = 3(3, 2, 0, 13) = (9, 6, 0, 39)$$

and

$$3(1, 3, 5, 7) + 3(2, -1, -5, 6) = (3, 9, 15, 21) + (6, -3, -15, 18)$$
$$= (9, 6, 0, 39),$$

which illustrates the first distributive property. Also

$$(3 + 4)(2, -1, -5, 6) = 7(2, -1, -5, 6) = (14, -7, -35, 42)$$

and

$$3(2, -1, -5, 6) + 4(2, -1, -5, 6) = (6, -3, -15, 18) + (8, -4, -20, 24)$$
$$= (14, -7, -35, 42),$$

which illustrates the second.

Let us now look at another, apparently very different, set of elements. This is the set of *quadratic polynomials*, namely, functions of the form

$$p : \mathbb{R} \longrightarrow \mathbb{R}$$
$$x \longmapsto a + bx + cx^2,$$

where $a, b, c \in \mathbb{R}$. We call this set P_3 because the rule $a + bx + cx^2$ has three terms. Thus

$$P_3 = \{p(x) : p(x) = a + bx + cx^2, \ a, b, c \in \mathbb{R}\}.$$

Here we have used the convention that when a real function is specified only by a rule, it is understood that the domain of the function is the set of all real numbers for which the rule is applicable, and the codomain of the function is $\mathbb{R}$.

Unit I1

To simplify the notation further, we write

$$P_3 = \{a + bx + cx^2 : a, b, c \in \mathbb{R}\}.$$

We often make this simplification when dealing with sets of real functions.

This set includes the linear polynomials (where c is 0) and constants (where b and c are 0). At first sight, there is no reason why this set of elements should have the properties that we have just shown are satisfied by $\mathbb{R}^4$, however these properties all hold for this set as well. We shall check some of them, and ask you to check the rest.

First we consider the properties involving addition.

We showed that $\mathbb{R}^4$ is closed under addition; now we show that P_3 is also closed under addition of functions, as follows.

If $p_1(x) = a_1 + b_1 x + c_1 x^2$ and $p_2(x) = a_2 + b_2 x + c_2 x^2$, then

$$p_1(x) + p_2(x) = (a_1 + b_1 x + c_1 x^2) + (a_2 + b_2 x + c_2 x^2)$$
$$= (a_1 + a_2) + (b_1 + b_2)x + (c_1 + c_2)x^2,$$

which also belongs to P_3. So P_3 is *closed under addition*.

For example, $3 + 4x - 2x^2$ and $5 - 3x + 7x^2$ both belong to P_3, and

$$(3 + 4x - 2x^2) + (5 - 3x + 7x^2) = 8 + x + 5x^2,$$

which also belongs to P_3. In the next exercise we ask you to check the other addition properties.

Exercise 1.3   In P_3, let $p_1(x) = a_1 + b_1 x + c_1 x^2$, $p_2(x) = a_2 + b_2 x + c_2 x^2$ and $p_3(x) = a_3 + b_3 x + c_3 x^2$. Verify that the following results hold.

(a) $p_1(x) + p_2(x) = p_2(x) + p_1(x)$ (commutative law).

(b) $(p_1(x) + p_2(x)) + p_3(x) = p_1(x) + (p_2(x) + p_3(x))$ (associative law).

(c) $p_1(x) + \mathbf{0} = \mathbf{0} + p_1(x) = p_1(x)$, where $\mathbf{0} = 0 + 0x + 0x^2$ is the zero polynomial in P_3.

(d) $p_1(x) + (-p_1(x)) = \mathbf{0}$.

So P_3 satisfies the same addition properties as $\mathbb{R}^4$; that is, P_3 is an Abelian group under addition.

We now show that P_3 is closed under scalar multiplication.

If $p(x) = a + bx + cx^2$ and $\alpha \in \mathbb{R}$, then

$$\alpha p(x) = \alpha(a + bx + cx^2) = (\alpha a) + (\alpha b)x + (\alpha c)x^2,$$

which also belongs to P_3. So P_3 is *closed under scalar multiplication.*

In the following exercise we ask you to check the remaining properties involving scalar multiplication, for a particular case.

Exercise 1.4   Let $p(x) = 1 - x + 2x^2$ and $\alpha = 2$, $\beta = -3$. Show that:

(a) $1 \times p(x) = p(x)$;   (b) $\alpha(\beta p(x)) = (\alpha\beta)p(x)$.

To finish looking at the properties of P_3, we state the distributive laws that connect addition and scalar multiplication; the proofs simply involve multiplying out brackets. For all $p_1(x), p_2(x) \in P_3$ and $\alpha, \beta \in \mathbb{R}$,

$$\alpha(p_1(x) + p_2(x)) = \alpha p_1(x) + \alpha p_2(x)$$

and

$$(\alpha + \beta)p_1(x) = \alpha p_1(x) + \beta p_1(x).$$

So $\mathbb{R}^4$ and P_3 satisfy the same set of properties with respect to addition and scalar multiplication, even though $\mathbb{R}^4$ is a Euclidean space and P_3 is a set of polynomials. The idea that connects them is the concept of a *vector space.*

In Group Theory Block A we studied symmetries of geometric figures, and then abstracted the properties to obtain the definition of a group. We go through a similar process here. We have just studied $\mathbb{R}^4$ and P_3, and we now abstract from them the definition of a vector space. We then go on to look at other examples of vector spaces. The elements of these vector spaces are of diverse types—complex numbers, functions, matrices, and many others.

The definition of a vector space is one of the longest definitions in mathematics. It looks formidable, but as you read it you will notice that the axioms A1–A5, S1–S3 and D1–D2 are the properties you checked for $\mathbb{R}^4$ and P_3. Thus this definition follows naturally from our previous examples. Axioms A1–A5 refer to vector addition, S1–S3 to scalar multiplication, and D1–D2 to how we combine these operations.

Definition   A **real vector space** consists of a set V of elements and two operations, vector addition and scalar multiplication, such that the following axioms hold.

A1 CLOSURE   For all $\mathbf{v}_1, \mathbf{v}_2 \in V$,
$$\mathbf{v}_1 + \mathbf{v}_2 \in V.$$

A2 IDENTITY   For each $\mathbf{v} \in V$, there is a zero element $\mathbf{0} \in V$ satisfying
$$\mathbf{v} + \mathbf{0} = \mathbf{0} + \mathbf{v} = \mathbf{v}.$$

A3 INVERSES   For each $\mathbf{v} \in V$, there is an element $-\mathbf{v}$ (its additive inverse) such that
$$\mathbf{v} + (-\mathbf{v}) = -\mathbf{v} + \mathbf{v} = \mathbf{0}.$$

A4 ASSOCIATIVITY   For all $\mathbf{v}_1, \mathbf{v}_2, \mathbf{v}_3 \in V$,
$$(\mathbf{v}_1 + \mathbf{v}_2) + \mathbf{v}_3 = \mathbf{v}_1 + (\mathbf{v}_2 + \mathbf{v}_3).$$

A5 COMMUTATIVITY   For all $\mathbf{v}_1, \mathbf{v}_2 \in V$,
$$\mathbf{v}_1 + \mathbf{v}_2 = \mathbf{v}_2 + \mathbf{v}_1.$$

S1 CLOSURE   For all $\mathbf{v} \in V$ and $\alpha \in \mathbb{R}$,
$$\alpha \mathbf{v} \in V.$$

S2 ASSOCIATIVITY   For all $\mathbf{v} \in V$ and $\alpha, \beta \in \mathbb{R}$,
$$\alpha(\beta \mathbf{v}) = (\alpha\beta)\mathbf{v}.$$

S3 IDENTITY   For all $\mathbf{v} \in V$,
$$1\mathbf{v} = \mathbf{v}.$$

D1 DISTRIBUTIVITY   For all $\mathbf{v}_1, \mathbf{v}_2 \in V$ and $\alpha \in \mathbb{R}$,
$$\alpha(\mathbf{v}_1 + \mathbf{v}_2) = \alpha \mathbf{v}_1 + \alpha \mathbf{v}_2.$$

D2 DISTRIBUTIVITY   For all $\mathbf{v} \in V$ and $\alpha, \beta \in \mathbb{R}$,
$$(\alpha + \beta)\mathbf{v} = \alpha \mathbf{v} + \beta \mathbf{v}.$$

The word 'real' in this definition refers to the fact that *the scalars used in forming scalar multiples are real numbers*. It is also possible to form complex and rational vector spaces, where the elements are scalar-multiplied by complex and rational numbers, respectively.

Axioms A1–A5 tell us that $(V, +)$ is an *Abelian group*.

Remark   In this definition we use the term element, whereas when we considered $\mathbb{R}^n$ we used the term vector. Both these terms are used interchangeably in many mathematical texts. In this section we use the term *vector* when we are considering vectors in $\mathbb{R}^n$, and the term *element* otherwise. Subsequently, the term *vector* will be used whatever the vector space under consideration.

We now look at another set of functions, and show that it is a vector space by testing all the axioms in the definition.

Example 1.3   Show that the set $V = \{a \cos x + b \sin x : a, b \in \mathbb{R}\}$ is a real vector space, by checking the axioms A1–A5, S1–S3 and D1–D2.

Solution

A1 V is closed under addition of functions, since, if $a_1 \cos x + b_1 \sin x$ and $a_2 \cos x + b_2 \sin x$ are elements of V, then
$$(a_1 \cos x + b_1 \sin x) + (a_2 \cos x + b_2 \sin x)$$
$$= (a_1 + a_2) \cos x + (b_1 + b_2) \sin x,$$
which is an element of V.

We shall *not* ask you to check *all* these axioms in any exercises; we have included this example simply to show how it can be done.

For example,
$$(3 \cos x + 2 \sin x)$$
$$+ (4 \cos x - 6 \sin x)$$
$$= 7 \cos x - 4 \sin x.$$

A2   The zero element is $0\cos x + 0\sin x$, since, if $a\cos x + b\sin x \in V$, then

$$(a\cos x + b\sin x) + (0\cos x + 0\sin x) = a\cos x + b\sin x$$

and

$$(0\cos x + 0\sin x) + (a\cos x + b\sin x) = a\cos x + b\sin x.$$

A3   The additive inverse of $a\cos x + b\sin x$ is $-a\cos x - b\sin x$, since, if $a\cos x + b\sin x \in V$, then

$$(a\cos x + b\sin x) + (-a\cos x - b\sin x) = 0\cos x + 0\sin x$$

and

$$(-a\cos x - b\sin x) + (a\cos x + b\sin x) = 0\cos x + 0\sin x.$$

A4   Addition is associative, since, if $a_1\cos x + b_1\sin x$, $a_2\cos x + b_2\sin x$ and $a_3\cos x + b_3\sin x$ are elements of V, then

$$((a_1\cos x + b_1\sin x) + (a_2\cos x + b_2\sin x)) + (a_3\cos x + b_3\sin x)$$
$$= ((a_1 + a_2)\cos x + (b_1 + b_2)\sin x) + (a_3\cos x + b_3\sin x)$$
$$= (a_1 + a_2 + a_3)\cos x + (b_1 + b_2 + b_3)\sin x$$

and

$$(a_1\cos x + b_1\sin x) + ((a_2\cos x + b_2\sin x) + (a_3\cos x + b_3\sin x))$$
$$= (a_1\cos x + b_1\sin x) + ((a_2 + a_3)\cos x + (b_2 + b_3)\sin x)$$
$$= (a_1 + a_2 + a_3)\cos x + (b_1 + b_2 + b_3)\sin x.$$

A5   Addition is commutative, since, if $a_1\cos x + b_1\sin x$ and $a_2\cos x + b_2\sin x$ are elements of V, then

$$(a_1\cos x + b_1\sin x) + (a_2\cos x + b_2\sin x)$$
$$= (a_1 + a_2)\cos x + (b_1 + b_2)\sin x$$

and

$$(a_2\cos x + b_2\sin x) + (a_1\cos x + b_1\sin x)$$
$$= (a_2 + a_1)\cos x + (b_2 + b_1)\sin x.$$

S1 V is closed under scalar multiplication, since, for $a\cos x + b\sin x \in V$ and $\alpha \in \mathbb{R}$, we have

$$\alpha(a\cos x + b\sin x) = \alpha a\cos x + \alpha b\sin x.$$

This is in V, since $\alpha a, \alpha b \in \mathbb{R}$.

For example,
$$5(3\cos x + 4\sin x)$$
$$= 15\cos x + 20\sin x.$$

S2   For $\alpha, \beta \in \mathbb{R}$ and $a\cos x + b\sin x \in V$, we have

$$\alpha\left(\beta(a\cos x + b\sin x)\right) = \alpha(\beta a\cos x + \beta b\sin x)$$
$$= \alpha\beta a\cos x + \alpha\beta b\sin x$$
$$= (\alpha\beta)(a\cos x + b\sin x).$$

S3   For all $a\cos x + b\sin x \in V$,

$$1(a\cos x + b\sin x) = a\cos x + b\sin x.$$

D1   For all $\alpha \in \mathbb{R}$ and all $a_1\cos x + b_1\sin x$ and $a_2\cos x + b_2\sin x$ in V, we have

$$\alpha\left((a_1\cos x + b_1\sin x) + (a_2\cos x + b_2\sin x)\right)$$
$$= \alpha\left((a_1 + a_2)\cos x + (b_1 + b_2)\sin x\right)$$
$$= \alpha(a_1 + a_2)\cos x + \alpha(b_1 + b_2)\sin x$$

and

$$\alpha(a_1\cos x + b_1\sin x) + \alpha(a_2\cos x + b_2\sin x)$$
$$= \alpha a_1\cos x + \alpha a_2\cos x + \alpha b_1\sin x + \alpha b_2\sin x$$
$$= \alpha(a_1 + a_2)\cos x + \alpha(b_1 + b_2)\sin x.$$

D2   For all $\alpha, \beta \in \mathbb{R}$ and $a \cos x + b \sin x \in V$, we have

$$(\alpha + \beta)(a \cos x + b \sin x)$$
$$= (\alpha + \beta)a \cos x + (\alpha + \beta)b \sin x$$
$$= \alpha a \cos x + \beta a \cos x + \alpha b \sin x + \beta b \sin x$$

and

$$\alpha(a \cos x + b \sin x) + \beta(a \cos x + b \sin x)$$
$$= \alpha a \cos x + \alpha b \sin x + \beta a \cos x + \beta b \sin x.$$

Since all the vector space properties are satisfied, V is a vector space. ∎

We now look briefly at some further examples of vector spaces, to give you some idea of the different areas of mathematics in which this concept arises.

The set of linear polynomials P_2

The elements in P_2 are polynomials of the form $p(x) = a + bx$, where $a, b \in \mathbb{R}$. Addition and scalar multiplication are defined as follows.

We call this P_2 by analogy with P_3 earlier.

If $p(x) = a + bx$ and $q(x) = c + dx$, and $\alpha \in \mathbb{R}$, then

$$p(x) + q(x) = (a + bx) + (c + dx) = (a + c) + (b + d)x$$

and

$$\alpha p(x) = \alpha(a + bx) = (\alpha a) + (\alpha b)x.$$

The result of each of these operations is a linear polynomial, so P_2 is closed under the operations of addition and scalar multiplication, and therefore satisfies A1 and S1. The other axioms can be checked in the same way.

More generally, for each positive integer n, the set P_n of real polynomials of degree less than n, with the usual operations of addition and scalar multiplication, is a vector space.

The set of complex numbers $\mathbb{C}$

The elements in $\mathbb{C}$ are numbers of the form $a + bi$, where $i^2 = -1$ and $a, b \in \mathbb{R}$. Vector addition and scalar multiplication are defined as

$$(a + bi) + (c + di) = (a + c) + (b + d)i$$

and

$$\alpha(a + bi) = (\alpha a) + (\alpha b)i.$$

In this case we multiply the *complex* number (the element) by a *real* number (the scalar).

The result of each of these operations is a complex number, so $\mathbb{C}$ is closed under the operations of vector addition and scalar multiplication, and therefore satisfies A1 and S1. The other axioms can be checked in the same way.

The set of 2×3 matrices with real entries

Vector addition and scalar multiplication are defined as follows.

If $\mathbf{A} = \begin{pmatrix} a_1 & a_2 & a_3 \\ a_4 & a_5 & a_6 \end{pmatrix}$ and $\mathbf{B} = \begin{pmatrix} b_1 & b_2 & b_3 \\ b_4 & b_5 & b_6 \end{pmatrix}$, and $\alpha \in \mathbb{R}$, then

$$\mathbf{A} + \mathbf{B} = \begin{pmatrix} a_1 & a_2 & a_3 \\ a_4 & a_5 & a_6 \end{pmatrix} + \begin{pmatrix} b_1 & b_2 & b_3 \\ b_4 & b_5 & b_6 \end{pmatrix}$$
$$= \begin{pmatrix} a_1 + b_1 & a_2 + b_2 & a_3 + b_3 \\ a_4 + b_4 & a_5 + b_5 & a_6 + b_6 \end{pmatrix}$$

and

$$\alpha \mathbf{A} = \alpha \begin{pmatrix} a_1 & a_2 & a_3 \\ a_4 & a_5 & a_6 \end{pmatrix} = \begin{pmatrix} \alpha a_1 & \alpha a_2 & \alpha a_3 \\ \alpha a_4 & \alpha a_5 & \alpha a_6 \end{pmatrix}.$$

The result of each of these operations is a 2×3 matrix, so this set is closed under the operations of vector addition and scalar multiplication, and therefore satisfies A1 and S1. The other axioms can be checked in the same way.

More generally, for positive integers m and n, the set $M_{m,n}$ of $m \times n$ matrices with real entries is a vector space under the operations of vector addition and scalar multiplication defined in Unit LA1.

The set $\mathbb{R}^\infty$

If $\mathbf{u} = (u_1, u_2, \dots)$ and $\mathbf{v} = (v_1, v_2, \dots)$ belong to $\mathbb{R}^\infty$, and $\alpha \in \mathbb{R}$, then

$$\mathbf{u} + \mathbf{v} = (u_1, u_2, \dots) + (v_1, v_2, \dots) = (u_1 + v_1, u_2 + v_2, \dots)$$

and

$$\alpha \mathbf{u} = \alpha(u_1, u_2, \dots) = (\alpha u_1, \alpha u_2, \dots).$$

The result of each of these operations is an element of $\mathbb{R}^\infty$, so $\mathbb{R}^\infty$ is closed under the operations of vector addition and scalar multiplication, and therefore satisfies A1 and S1. The other axioms can be checked in the same way.

These examples are only a few of the many real vector spaces. You will meet more of them as you work through this unit, and as you encounter other mathematical concepts in the remainder of this course.

We finish the section with another example and exercise.

Example 1.4   Show that neither of the following sets is a real vector space.

(a) $V = \{$all polynomials of degree equal to 5$\}$

(b) $V = \{a + bi \in \mathbb{C} : a \geq 0\}$

We assume the usual definitions of addition and scalar multiplication for elements of these sets.

Solution

(a) Addition on the set of all polynomials of degree equal to five fails to satisfy A1.

A counter-example for A1 is given by $p(x) = x + x^5$, $q(x) = x - x^5$.

Then $p(x) + q(x) = (x + x^5) + (x - x^5) = 2x$, which is a polynomial of degree 1.

Other axioms also fail, or do not make sense; for example, V contains no zero element.

(b) Scalar multiplication on the set of complex numbers of the form $a + bi$, where $a \geq 0$, fails to satisfy S1.

A counter-example for S1 is given by $z = 1 + i$, $\alpha = -1$.

Then $\alpha z = -1 - i$, which is not of the form $a + bi$ where $a \geq 0$. ∎

Exercise 1.5   Show that neither of the following sets is a real vector space.

(a) $V = \{(x, y) \in \mathbb{R}^2 : y = 2x + 1\}$

(b) $V = \left\{ \begin{pmatrix} 0 & a \\ b & c \end{pmatrix} : a, b, c \in \mathbb{Z} \right\}$

Further exercise

Exercise 1.6   Show that the following are not vector spaces, by finding an axiom that fails. Assume the usual definitions of addition and scalar multiplication for the elements of these sets.

(a) $V = \{2 + ax : a \in \mathbb{R}\}$

(b) $V = \{(x, y, x + y - 3) \in \mathbb{R}^3 : x, y \in \mathbb{R}\}$

(c) $V = \{(x, y) : x \geq 0, \ x, y \in \mathbb{R}\}$

(d) $V = \left\{ \begin{pmatrix} a & b \\ c & d \end{pmatrix} : ad - bc = 1 \right\}$

2   Linear combinations and spanning sets

After working through this section, you should be able to:

(a) explain the meaning of the terms *linear combination*, *span* and *spanning set*;

(b) form linear combinations of vectors in a given set;

(c) check whether a vector can be expressed as a linear combination of given vectors;

(d) find the set spanned by a given set of vectors;

(e) check whether a given set of vectors spans the vector space to which the vectors belong.

2.1 Linear combinations

We begin by looking at the different ways in which we can express a single vector in $\mathbb{R}^2$ as a combination of two other vectors.

For example, the vector $(5, 3)$ can be written as

$$(5, 3) = 5(1, 0) + 3(0, 1).$$

We could also write $(5, 3)$ in terms of $(2, 0)$ and $(1, 1)$. In this case we have

$$(5, 3) = 1(2, 0) + 3(1, 1).$$

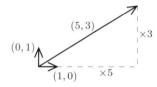

If you look at the right-hand sides of these equations, you will see that they both have the same form. In each case we have written

$$(5, 3) = \alpha \mathbf{v}_1 + \beta \mathbf{v}_2,$$

where $\mathbf{v}_1 = (1, 0)$, $\mathbf{v}_2 = (0, 1)$, $\alpha = 5$ and $\beta = 3$ in the first case, and $\mathbf{v}_1 = (2, 0)$, $\mathbf{v}_2 = (1, 1)$, $\alpha = 1$ and $\beta = 3$ in the second case.

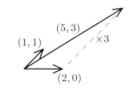

We call $\alpha \mathbf{v}_1 + \beta \mathbf{v}_2$ a *linear combination* of the two vectors $\mathbf{v}_1$ and $\mathbf{v}_2$.

Because $\mathbf{v}_1$ and $\mathbf{v}_2$ are vectors in $\mathbb{R}^2$, so are $\alpha \mathbf{v}_1$ and $\beta \mathbf{v}_2$, since they are scalar multiples of $\mathbf{v}_1$ and $\mathbf{v}_2$; and hence so is $\alpha \mathbf{v}_1 + \beta \mathbf{v}_2$, since it is the sum of two vectors in $\mathbb{R}^2$. So $\alpha \mathbf{v}_1 + \beta \mathbf{v}_2$ is also a vector in $\mathbb{R}^2$.

Similarly in $\mathbb{R}^3$, the vector $(-1, -4, 4)$ can be written as

$$(-1, -4, 4) = -1(1, 0, 0) - 4(0, 1, 0) + 4(0, 0, 1)$$

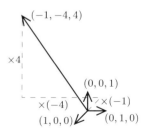

or as

$$(-1, -4, 4) = 2(1, 0, 2) + 1(0, -1, 3) - 3(1, 1, 1).$$

Each of these equations has the form

$$(-1, -4, 4) = \alpha \mathbf{v}_1 + \beta \mathbf{v}_2 + \gamma \mathbf{v}_3,$$

where the expression on the right-hand side of the equation is a *linear combination* of three vectors.

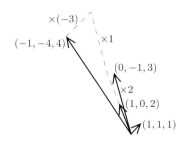

These linear combinations of vectors in $\mathbb{R}^2$ and $\mathbb{R}^3$ are particular examples of the following definition.

Definition   Let $\mathbf{v}_1, \mathbf{v}_2, \ldots, \mathbf{v}_k$ belong to a vector space V. Then a **linear combination** of the vectors $\mathbf{v}_1, \mathbf{v}_2, \ldots, \mathbf{v}_k$ is a vector of the form

$$\alpha_1 \mathbf{v}_1 + \alpha_2 \mathbf{v}_2 + \cdots + \alpha_k \mathbf{v}_k,$$

where $\alpha_1, \alpha_2, \ldots, \alpha_k$ are real numbers. This vector also belongs to V.

We begin by looking at how we can form linear combinations of vectors, and then investigate whether we can write a particular vector as a linear combination of other vectors in the same vector space.

In the examples and exercises of this section we have tried to keep the arithmetic simple by using *integer* scalar multiples and coordinates. In practice, any real numbers may occur.

Example 2.1

(a) In $\mathbb{R}^3$, calculate the linear combination $2\mathbf{v}_1 + 3\mathbf{v}_2$ when $\mathbf{v}_1 = (1, 0, 3)$ and $\mathbf{v}_2 = (0, 2, -1)$.

(b) In $\mathbb{R}^4$, calculate the linear combination $2\mathbf{v}_1 + 3\mathbf{v}_2 + 4\mathbf{v}_3 - \mathbf{v}_4$ when $\mathbf{v}_1 = (1, 0, 3, 1)$, $\mathbf{v}_2 = (0, 2, 0, -1)$, $\mathbf{v}_3 = (0, 1, -2, 0)$ and $\mathbf{v}_4 = (2, 10, -2, -1)$.

Solution

(a) $2\mathbf{v}_1 + 3\mathbf{v}_2 = 2(1, 0, 3) + 3(0, 2, -1) = (2, 0, 6) + (0, 6, -3) = (2, 6, 3)$

(b) $2\mathbf{v}_1 + 3\mathbf{v}_2 + 4\mathbf{v}_3 - \mathbf{v}_4$
$= 2(1, 0, 3, 1) + 3(0, 2, 0, -1) + 4(0, 1, -2, 0) - (2, 10, -2, -1)$
$= (2, 0, 6, 2) + (0, 6, 0, -3) + (0, 4, -8, 0) - (2, 10, -2, -1)$
$= (0, 0, 0, 0)$ ∎

Exercise 2.1

(a) In $\mathbb{R}^2$, let $\mathbf{v}_1 = (0, 3)$ and $\mathbf{v}_2 = (2, 1)$. Calculate the linear combination $4\mathbf{v}_1 - 2\mathbf{v}_2$.

(b) In $\mathbb{R}^4$, let $\mathbf{v}_1 = (1, 2, 1, 3)$ and $\mathbf{v}_2 = (2, 1, 0, -1)$. Calculate the linear combination $3\mathbf{v}_1 + 2\mathbf{v}_2$.

We now look at linear combinations of vectors in vector spaces other than $\mathbb{R}^2$, $\mathbb{R}^3$ and $\mathbb{R}^4$. In the example and exercise which follow, we assume that the operations of vector addition and scalar multiplication for polynomials, matrices and functions are the usual ones.

Example 2.2   For each of the following vector spaces V and vectors $\mathbf{v}_1, \mathbf{v}_2$ and $\mathbf{v}_3$ in V, form the linear combination $3\mathbf{v}_1 - 2\mathbf{v}_2 + \mathbf{v}_3$.

(a) $V = P_3$, $\mathbf{v}_1 = 1 + x + x^2$, $\mathbf{v}_2 = 1 - x$, $\mathbf{v}_3 = x + x^2$.

(b) $V = M_{2,3}$, $\mathbf{v}_1 = \begin{pmatrix} 1 & 0 & 2 \\ 0 & -1 & 3 \end{pmatrix}$, $\mathbf{v}_2 = \begin{pmatrix} 2 & -1 & 0 \\ 0 & 3 & -4 \end{pmatrix}$,

$\mathbf{v}_3 = \begin{pmatrix} -1 & 0 & 0 \\ 0 & 2 & 1 \end{pmatrix}$.

Solution

(a) $3\mathbf{v}_1 - 2\mathbf{v}_2 + \mathbf{v}_3 = 3(1 + x + x^2) - 2(1 - x) + (x + x^2) = 1 + 6x + 4x^2$

(b) $3\mathbf{v}_1 - 2\mathbf{v}_2 + \mathbf{v}_3 = 3\begin{pmatrix} 1 & 0 & 2 \\ 0 & -1 & 3 \end{pmatrix} - 2\begin{pmatrix} 2 & -1 & 0 \\ 0 & 3 & -4 \end{pmatrix} + \begin{pmatrix} -1 & 0 & 0 \\ 0 & 2 & 1 \end{pmatrix}$

$= \begin{pmatrix} -2 & 2 & 6 \\ 0 & -7 & 18 \end{pmatrix}$ ■

Exercise 2.2   For each of the following vector spaces V and vectors $\mathbf{v}_1$ and $\mathbf{v}_2$ in V, form the linear combination $2\mathbf{v}_1 - 4\mathbf{v}_2$.

(a) $V = P_3$, $\mathbf{v}_1 = 2 - x + 3x^2$, $\mathbf{v}_2 = -1 + x$.

(b) V is the set of real functions, $\mathbf{v}_1 = \sin x$ and $\mathbf{v}_2 = x \cos x$.

(c) $V = M_{2,2}$, $\mathbf{v}_1 = \begin{pmatrix} -1 & 1 \\ 2 & 0 \end{pmatrix}$, $\mathbf{v}_2 = \begin{pmatrix} 3 & 1 \\ 0 & -2 \end{pmatrix}$.

Now that we have formed linear combinations of different numbers of vectors in various vector spaces, we consider the harder problem of deciding whether we can express a given vector as a linear combination of a particular set of vectors. We look at an example before giving a general strategy.

Example 2.3   Determine whether $(3, -1)$ can be expressed as a linear combination of each of the following.

(a) $\mathbf{v}_1 = (2, 0)$ and $\mathbf{v}_2 = (1, 1)$.

(b) $\mathbf{v}_1 = (2, 2)$ and $\mathbf{v}_2 = (1, 1)$.

(c) $\mathbf{v}_1 = (9, -3)$ and $\mathbf{v}_2 = (-6, 2)$.

Solution

(a) We need to find real numbers α and β such that

$$(3, -1) = \alpha(2, 0) + \beta(1, 1),$$

that is,

$$(3, -1) = (2\alpha + \beta, \beta).$$

If we equate the two first coordinates and then the two second coordinates, we obtain the simultaneous linear equations

$$\begin{cases} 2\alpha + \beta = 3, \\ \beta = -1. \end{cases}$$

Substituting $\beta = -1$ in the first equation gives $\alpha = 2$. So

$$(3, -1) = 2(2, 0) - 1(1, 1) = 2\mathbf{v}_1 - \mathbf{v}_2.$$

This representation of $(3, -1)$ is shown in the diagram in the margin.

(b) We need to find real numbers α and β such that

$$(3, -1) = \alpha(2, 2) + \beta(1, 1),$$

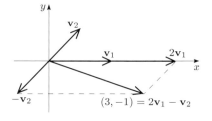

that is,

$$(3, -1) = (2\alpha + \beta, 2\alpha + \beta).$$

If we equate the two first coordinates and then the two second coordinates, we obtain the simultaneous equations

$$\begin{cases} 2\alpha + \beta = \ \ \ 3, \\ 2\alpha + \beta = -1. \end{cases}$$

This pair of equations is inconsistent, since no values of α and β satisfy both of them, and so we cannot express $(3, -1)$ as a linear combination of these two vectors.

You may have noticed that any linear combination of $(1, 1)$ and $(2, 2)$ must have both coordinates the same.

(c) We need to find real numbers α and β such that

$$(3, -1) = \alpha(9, -3) + \beta(-6, 2),$$

that is,

$$(3, -1) = (9\alpha - 6\beta, -3\alpha + 2\beta).$$

If we equate the two first coordinates and then the two second coordinates, we obtain the simultaneous equations

$$\begin{cases} \ \ \ 9\alpha - 6\beta = \ \ \ 3, \\ -3\alpha + 2\beta = -1. \end{cases}$$

These equations are equivalent to the single equation

$$3\alpha - 2\beta = 1,$$

so any values of α and β that satisfy this equation give a solution. Thus in this case there are infinitely many solutions. For example, if $\alpha = 1$, then $\beta = 1$, and

$$(3, -1) = (9, -3) + (-6, 2). \quad \blacksquare$$

Other solutions include
$$\alpha = \tfrac{1}{3}, \ \beta = 0;$$
$$\alpha = 0, \ \beta = -\tfrac{1}{2}.$$

In the following strategy we describe the method we have just used.

Strategy 2.1 To determine whether a given vector $\mathbf{v}$ can be written as a linear combination of the vectors $\mathbf{v}_1, \mathbf{v}_2, \ldots, \mathbf{v}_k$.

1. Write $\mathbf{v} = \alpha_1 \mathbf{v}_1 + \alpha_2 \mathbf{v}_2 + \cdots + \alpha_k \mathbf{v}_k$.

2. Use this expression to write down a system of simultaneous linear equations in the unknowns $\alpha_1, \alpha_2, \ldots, \alpha_k$.

3. Solve the resulting system of equations, if possible.

Then $\mathbf{v}$ can be written as a linear combination of $\mathbf{v}_1, \mathbf{v}_2, \ldots, \mathbf{v}_k$ if and only if the system has a solution.

Because this strategy involves solving simultaneous linear equations, there may be no solution, a unique solution, or infinitely many solutions, as we saw in Example 2.3.

You saw how to solve simultaneous linear equations in Unit LA2.

Example 2.4

(a) In $\mathbb{R}^3$, express the vector $(1, 1, 1)$ as a linear combination of the vectors $(1, 0, 1)$, $(0, 1, 2)$ and $(-1, 1, 0)$.

(b) In P_3, express the polynomial $2 + 2x + 5x^2$ as a linear combination of the polynomials $1 + 3x^2$ and $2x - x^2$.

Solution   We follow the steps of Strategy 2.1.

(a) Let α, β and γ be real numbers such that   Step 1

$$(1,1,1) = \alpha(1,0,1) + \beta(0,1,2) + \gamma(-1,1,0).$$

Then

$$(1,1,1) = (\alpha - \gamma, \beta + \gamma, \alpha + 2\beta).$$

Equating corresponding coordinates, we obtain the simultaneous   Step 2
equations

$$\begin{cases} \alpha \qquad - \gamma = 1, \\ \qquad \beta + \gamma = 1, \\ \alpha + 2\beta \qquad = 1. \end{cases}$$

Adding the first two equations gives $\alpha + \beta = 2$, and solving this and   Step 3
the last equation gives $\beta = -1$ and $\alpha = 3$. Substitution then gives
$\gamma = 2$, so the required linear combination is

$$(1,1,1) = 3(1,0,1) - 1(0,1,2) + 2(-1,1,0).$$

(b) Let α and β be real numbers such that   Step 1

$$2 + 2x + 5x^2 = \alpha(1 + 3x^2) + \beta(2x - x^2).$$

Then

$$2 + 2x + 5x^2 = \alpha + (2\beta)x + (3\alpha - \beta)x^2.$$

Equating corresponding coefficients, we obtain the simultaneous   Step 2
equations

$$\begin{cases} \alpha \qquad = 2, \\ \quad 2\beta = 2, \\ 3\alpha - \beta = 5. \end{cases}$$

The first two equations have the solution $\alpha = 2$, $\beta = 1$, and this   Step 3
solution also satisfies the third equation. So the required linear   It is important to check that *all*
combination is   the equations are satisfied;
                                                                            otherwise, there is no solution.
$$2 + 2x + 5x^2 = 2(1 + 3x^2) + (2x - x^2). \quad \blacksquare$$

Exercise 2.3

(a) In $\mathbb{R}^2$, express the vector $(2,4)$ as a linear combination of the
vectors $(0,3)$ and $(2,1)$.

(b) In $\mathbb{R}^3$, express the vector $(2,3,-2)$ as a linear combination of the
vectors $(0,1,0)$, $(1,2,-1)$ and $(1,1,-2)$.

(c) In $M_{2,2}$, express the matrix $\begin{pmatrix} 3 & 1 \\ 0 & 4 \end{pmatrix}$ as a linear combination of

the matrices $\begin{pmatrix} 1 & -1 \\ 0 & 2 \end{pmatrix}$ and $\begin{pmatrix} 0 & -2 \\ 0 & 1 \end{pmatrix}$.

2.2 Spanning sets

We now look at the set of vectors that is produced when we form *all*
possible linear combinations of a given set of vectors.

Picture any two vectors in $\mathbb{R}^2$, and suppose that we form all possible linear
combinations of these two vectors. What vectors do we obtain? Are there
any vectors in $\mathbb{R}^2$ that *cannot* be written as a linear combination of these
two vectors? What happens if we start with one vector in $\mathbb{R}^2$? If we form

all possible linear combinations of it, what vectors can result? What happens if we start with one, two or three vectors in $\mathbb{R}^3$?

Let us start with a set consisting of exactly one vector in $\mathbb{R}^2$—namely, the set containing the vector $(1,0)$. The set of all linear combinations of $(1,0)$ is

$$\{\alpha(1,0) : \alpha \in \mathbb{R}\} = \{(\alpha, 0) : \alpha \in \mathbb{R}\}.$$

Geometrically, the members of this set are the points on the x-axis in $\mathbb{R}^2$. So this set of linear combinations is a line (the x-axis) in $\mathbb{R}^2$. We say that the set $\{(1,0)\}$ *spans* the x-axis, and that the x-axis is *spanned* by $\{(1,0)\}$.

Suppose that we now take the set $\{(1,0), (0,1)\}$ containing two vectors. The set of all linear combinations of $(1,0)$ and $(0,1)$ is

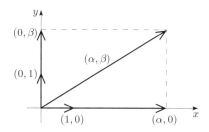

$$\{\alpha(1,0) + \beta(0,1) : \alpha, \beta \in \mathbb{R}\} = \{(\alpha, \beta) : \alpha, \beta \in \mathbb{R}\}.$$

Since α and β can take any real values, this set consists of all the points in $\mathbb{R}^2$. We say that $\{(1,0), (0,1)\}$ *spans* $\mathbb{R}^2$, and that $\mathbb{R}^2$ is *spanned* by $\{(1,0), (0,1)\}$.

We now write down the formal definitions of span and spanning, before looking at some more examples.

Definition   Let $S = \{\mathbf{v}_1, \mathbf{v}_2, \ldots, \mathbf{v}_k\}$ be a finite set of vectors in a vector space V. Then the **span** $\langle S \rangle$ of S is the set of all possible linear combinations

$$\alpha_1 \mathbf{v}_1 + \alpha_2 \mathbf{v}_2 + \cdots + \alpha_k \mathbf{v}_k,$$

where $\alpha_1, \alpha_2, \ldots, \alpha_k$ are real numbers; that is,

$$\langle S \rangle = \{\alpha_1 \mathbf{v}_1 + \alpha_2 \mathbf{v}_2 + \cdots + \alpha_k \mathbf{v}_k : \alpha_1, \alpha_2, \ldots, \alpha_k \in \mathbb{R}\}.$$

We say that the set of vectors $\{\mathbf{v}_1, \mathbf{v}_2, \ldots, \mathbf{v}_k\}$ **spans** $\langle S \rangle$ or is a **spanning set** for $\langle S \rangle$, and that $\langle S \rangle$ is the set **spanned** by S.

While S is a *finite* set of vectors, the span $\langle S \rangle$ is generally an infinite set of vectors (such as a line or plane). $\langle S \rangle$ is itself a vector space.

To test whether a vector $\mathbf{v}$ lies in the span of a given set S, we use Strategy 2.1 to determine whether $\mathbf{v}$ can be written as a linear combination of the vectors in S.

Example 2.5   Let $S = \{(1,1,0), (0,1,1)\}$. Which of the following vectors belong to $\langle S \rangle$?

(a) $(0,0,1)$ (b) $(4,2,-2)$

Solution   We follow the steps of Strategy 2.1.

(a) We write   Step 1

$$(0,0,1) = \alpha(1,1,0) + \beta(0,1,1) = (\alpha, \alpha + \beta, \beta).$$

Equating corresponding coordinates gives the simultaneous equations   Step 2

$$\begin{cases} \alpha & = 0, \\ \alpha + \beta & = 0, \\ \beta & = 1. \end{cases}$$

This system is inconsistent and therefore has no solution. So $(0,0,1)$ Step 3
does not belong to $\langle S \rangle$.

(b) We write   Step 1

$$(4,2,-2) = \alpha(1,1,0) + \beta(0,1,1) = (\alpha, \alpha + \beta, \beta).$$

Equating corresponding coordinates gives the simultaneous equations   Step 2

$$\begin{cases} \alpha & = & 4, \\ \alpha + \beta & = & 2, \\ \beta & = & -2. \end{cases}$$

The first and third equations give $\alpha = 4$ and $\beta = -2$, and these values   Step 3
also satisfy the second equation. So $(4, 2, -2)$ belongs to $\langle S \rangle$ and it can
be written as

$$(4, 2, -2) = 4(1, 1, 0) - 2(0, 1, 1). \quad \blacksquare$$

Exercise 2.4   In $\mathbb{R}^3$, let $\mathbf{v}_1 = (1, 0, 3)$, $\mathbf{v}_2 = (0, 2, 0)$ and $\mathbf{v}_3 = (0, 3, 1)$.
Use Strategy 2.1 to determine whether the vector $(1, 5, 4)$ lies in the
subset of $\mathbb{R}^3$ spanned by each of the following sets.

(a) $\{\mathbf{v}_1, \mathbf{v}_2\}$ (b) $\{\mathbf{v}_1, \mathbf{v}_2, \mathbf{v}_3\}$

Strategy 2.1 can also be used to show that a given set of vectors is a
spanning set for the whole of a particular vector space, as we see in the
following example.

Example 2.6   Show that each of the following is a spanning set for $\mathbb{R}^2$.

(a) $\{(1, 2), (2, -3)\}$ (b) $\{(1, 0), (1, 1), (1, -2)\}$

Solution

(a) Each vector in $\mathbb{R}^2$ can be written as (x, y). To show that (x, y) is in
$\langle \{(1, 2), (2, -3)\} \rangle$, we write   Step 1

$$(x, y) = \alpha(1, 2) + \beta(2, -3) = (\alpha + 2\beta, 2\alpha - 3\beta).$$

Equating corresponding coordinates gives the simultaneous equations   Step 2

$$\begin{cases} \alpha + 2\beta = x, \\ 2\alpha - 3\beta = y, \end{cases}$$

whose solutions are $\alpha = \frac{1}{7}(3x + 2y)$, $\beta = \frac{1}{7}(2x - y)$. So   Step 3

$$(x, y) = \tfrac{1}{7}(3x + 2y)(1, 2) + \tfrac{1}{7}(2x - y)(2, -3).$$

Thus $\{(1, 2), (2, -3)\}$ is a spanning set for $\mathbb{R}^2$; that is,

$$\langle \{(1, 2), (2, -3)\} \rangle = \mathbb{R}^2.$$

(b) Each vector in $\mathbb{R}^2$ can be written as (x, y). To show that (x, y) is in
$\langle \{(1, 0), (1, 1), (1, -2)\} \rangle$, we write   Step 1

$$(x, y) = \alpha(1, 0) + \beta(1, 1) + \gamma(1, -2) = (\alpha + \beta + \gamma, \beta - 2\gamma).$$

Equating corresponding coordinates gives the simultaneous equations   Step 2

$$\begin{cases} \alpha + \beta + \gamma = x, \\ \beta - 2\gamma = y. \end{cases}$$

This is a system of two linear equations in three unknowns, so it has
infinitely many solutions. For example, taking $\gamma = 0$ gives $\beta = y$ and   Step 3
$\alpha = x - y$. So

$$(x, y) = (x - y)(1, 0) + y(1, 1) + 0(1, -2).$$

Thus $\langle \{(1, 0), (1, 1), (1, -2)\} \rangle = \mathbb{R}^2$. $\quad \blacksquare$

The solution to Example 2.6(b) shows that the set $\{(1, 0), (1, 1)\}$ is a
spanning set for $\mathbb{R}^2$ and so, in some sense, the vector $(1, -2)$ is redundant.
We return to this idea of redundant vectors in a spanning set in the next
section.

Exercise 2.5 Show that each of the following is a spanning set for $\mathbb{R}^2$.

(a) $\{(1,1),(-1,2)\}$ (b) $\{(2,-1),(3,2)\}$

Exercise 2.6 Show that $\{(1,0,0),(1,1,0),(2,0,1)\}$ is a spanning set for $\mathbb{R}^3$.

We now give an example which shows that Strategy 2.1 can be used for vector spaces other than $\mathbb{R}^2$ and $\mathbb{R}^3$.

Example 2.7   Show that $\{1+x^2, x^2, 2-x\}$ is a spanning set for P_3.

Solution   Each polynomial in P_3 can be written as $a+bx+cx^2$. To   Step 1
show that $a+bx+cx^2$ is in $\langle\{1+x^2, x^2, 2-x\}\rangle$, we write

$$a+bx+cx^2 = \alpha(1+x^2) + \beta(x^2) + \gamma(2-x)$$
$$= \alpha + 2\gamma - \gamma x + (\alpha + \beta)x^2.$$

Equating corresponding coefficients gives the simultaneous equations   Step 2

$$\begin{cases} \alpha & + 2\gamma = a, \\ & - \gamma = b, \\ \alpha + \beta & = c. \end{cases}$$

It follows from the second equation that $\gamma = -b$. Substituting this into the   Step 3
first equation gives $\alpha = a + 2b$ and hence, from the third equation,
$\beta = c - a - 2b$. So

$$a+bx+cx^2 = (a+2b)(1+x^2) + (c-a-2b)x^2 - b(2-x).$$

Thus $\langle\{1+x^2, x^2, 2-x\}\rangle = P_3$. ∎

Exercise 2.7 Show that $\{1+x, 1+x^2, 1+x^3, x\}$ is a spanning set for P_4.

We look now at sets S in vector spaces V for which $\langle S\rangle$ is not the whole of V.

Example 2.8   For each of the following vector spaces V and sets of vectors S in V, determine $\langle S\rangle$. In parts (a) and (b), describe $\langle S\rangle$ geometrically.

(a) $V = \mathbb{R}^2$, $S = \{(1,1)\}$.

(b) $V = \mathbb{R}^3$, $S = \{(1,0,1),(2,0,3)\}$.

(c) $V = M_{2,3}$, $S = \left\{ \begin{pmatrix} 2 & -1 & 0 \\ 0 & 0 & 0 \end{pmatrix}, \begin{pmatrix} 1 & 0 & 3 \\ 0 & 0 & 0 \end{pmatrix}, \begin{pmatrix} 0 & -2 & 2 \\ 0 & 0 & 0 \end{pmatrix} \right\}$.

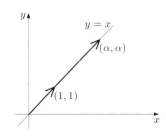

Solution

(a) In this case, $\langle S\rangle$ is the line $y = x$, since

$$\langle S\rangle = \{\alpha(1,1) : \alpha \in \mathbb{R}\} = \{(\alpha,\alpha) : \alpha \in \mathbb{R}\}.$$

(b) We have

$$\langle S\rangle = \{\alpha(1,0,1) + \beta(2,0,3) : \alpha, \beta \in \mathbb{R}\}$$
$$= \{(\alpha + 2\beta, 0, \alpha + 3\beta) : \alpha, \beta \in \mathbb{R}\}.$$

Thus

$$\langle S\rangle \subseteq \{(x,0,z) : x,z \in \mathbb{R}\}.$$

In fact, every vector $(x,0,z)$, $x,z \in \mathbb{R}$, belongs to $\langle S\rangle$. To show this, we write

$$(x,0,z) = (\alpha + 2\beta, 0, \alpha + 3\beta),$$

21

and equate corresponding coordinates to give the simultaneous equations

$$\begin{cases} \alpha + 2\beta = x, \\ \alpha + 3\beta = z. \end{cases}$$

The solution is $\beta = z - x$ and $\alpha = 3x - 2z$, so

$$(x, 0, z) = (3x - 2z)(1, 0, 1) + (z - x)(2, 0, 3).$$

Hence $(x, 0, z) \in \langle S \rangle$, so

$$\langle S \rangle = \{(x, 0, z) : x, z \in \mathbb{R}\},$$

which is the plane $y = 0$.

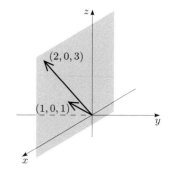

(c) We have

$$\langle S \rangle = \left\{ \alpha \begin{pmatrix} 2 & -1 & 0 \\ 0 & 0 & 0 \end{pmatrix} + \beta \begin{pmatrix} 1 & 0 & 3 \\ 0 & 0 & 0 \end{pmatrix} \right.$$
$$\left. + \gamma \begin{pmatrix} 0 & -2 & 2 \\ 0 & 0 & 0 \end{pmatrix} : \alpha, \beta, \gamma \in \mathbb{R} \right\}$$
$$= \left\{ \begin{pmatrix} 2\alpha + \beta & -\alpha - 2\gamma & 3\beta + 2\gamma \\ 0 & 0 & 0 \end{pmatrix} : \alpha, \beta, \gamma \in \mathbb{R} \right\}.$$

Thus

$$\langle S \rangle \subseteq \left\{ \begin{pmatrix} a & b & c \\ 0 & 0 & 0 \end{pmatrix} : a, b, c \in \mathbb{R} \right\}.$$

In fact, every 2×3 matrix with zero entries in the second row belongs to $\langle S \rangle$. To show this, we write

$$\begin{pmatrix} a & b & c \\ 0 & 0 & 0 \end{pmatrix} = \begin{pmatrix} 2\alpha + \beta & -\alpha - 2\gamma & 3\beta + 2\gamma \\ 0 & 0 & 0 \end{pmatrix},$$

and equate corresponding entries to give the simultaneous equations

$$\begin{cases} 2\alpha + \beta & = a, \\ -\alpha & - 2\gamma = b, \\ 3\beta + 2\gamma = c. \end{cases}$$

These have the solutions

$$\alpha = \tfrac{1}{7}(3a - b - c), \quad \beta = \tfrac{1}{7}(a + 2b + 2c), \quad \gamma = -\tfrac{1}{14}(3a + 6b - c),$$

so

$$\begin{pmatrix} a & b & c \\ 0 & 0 & 0 \end{pmatrix} \in \langle S \rangle.$$

Hence

$$\langle S \rangle = \left\{ \begin{pmatrix} a & b & c \\ 0 & 0 & 0 \end{pmatrix} : a, b, c \in \mathbb{R} \right\}. \quad \blacksquare$$

Exercise 2.8 For each of the following vector spaces V and sets of vectors S in V, determine $\langle S \rangle$.

(a) $V = \mathbb{R}^3$, $S = \{(1, 0, 0)\}$.

(b) $V = M_{2,2}$, $S = \left\{ \begin{pmatrix} 2 & 0 \\ 0 & 3 \end{pmatrix}, \begin{pmatrix} -1 & 0 \\ 0 & 2 \end{pmatrix} \right\}$.

Further exercises

Exercise 2.9 Calculate $2\mathbf{u} - \mathbf{v}$ for each of the following vectors $\mathbf{u}$ and $\mathbf{v}$, and draw a diagram in part (a) showing the resulting vector geometrically.

(a) In $\mathbb{R}^2$, $\mathbf{u} = (3, -1)$ and $\mathbf{v} = (2, 4)$.

(b) In $\mathbb{R}^3$, $\mathbf{u} = (1, 2, 0)$ and $\mathbf{v} = (0, -1, \frac{3}{4})$.

Exercise 2.10 Let $\mathbf{u} = (1, 0, 1)$, $\mathbf{v} = (-1, 1, 0)$, $\mathbf{w} = (0, 0, 1)$ and $\mathbf{z} = (1, 1, 0)$.

(a) Calculate the linear combination $2\mathbf{u} - \mathbf{v} + 3\mathbf{w}$.

(b) Find real numbers α, β, γ such that

$$\alpha\mathbf{u} + \beta\mathbf{v} + \gamma\mathbf{w} = (0, 1, 0).$$

(c) Do there exist real numbers α and β such that

$$\alpha\mathbf{u} + \beta\mathbf{v} = (0, 1, 0)?$$

(d) Find all possible real numbers α, β, γ and δ such that

$$\alpha\mathbf{u} + \beta\mathbf{v} + \gamma\mathbf{w} + \delta\mathbf{z} = (0, 1, 0).$$

Exercise 2.11 Let $S = \{(1, 1, 0), (0, 1, 1)\}$.

(a) Do the vectors $(0, 0, 1)$ and $(4, 2, -2)$ belong to the span $\langle S \rangle$?

(b) Give a simple geometric description of the span $\langle S \rangle$.

Exercise 2.12 Give a simple geometric description of the span $\langle S \rangle$ of the given sets.

(a) In $\mathbb{R}^2$, $S = \{(2, -1)\}$.

(b) In $\mathbb{R}^3$, $S = \{(0, -1, 1), (0, 2, -3)\}$.

Exercise 2.13 Give an algebraic description of the span $\langle S \rangle$ of the given sets.

(a) In P_3, $S = \{1 + 2x\}$.

(b) In $M_{2,2}$, $S = \left\{ \begin{pmatrix} 1 & 0 \\ 0 & 0 \end{pmatrix}, \begin{pmatrix} 0 & 0 \\ 0 & 3 \end{pmatrix} \right\}$.

Exercise 2.14 Show that the set $\{(-1, 0), (2, 1)\}$ spans $\mathbb{R}^2$.

3 Bases and dimension

After working through this section, you should be able to:

(a) explain the meaning of the terms *linear independence* and *linear dependence*, *basis* and *dimension*;

(b) test whether a given set of vectors is linearly independent;

(c) test whether a given set of vectors is a basis for a given vector space.

3.1 Linear independence and dependence

In Section 2 we found several spanning sets for $\mathbb{R}^2$ and $\mathbb{R}^3$. For example, we showed that each of the sets

$$\{(1,0),(1,1)\} \quad \text{and} \quad \{(1,0),(1,1),(1,-2)\}$$

Example 2.6

spans $\mathbb{R}^2$. In order to be able to work efficiently with a vector space, we need to express each vector in it as a linear combination of a small number of vectors. In particular, it would be convenient if we could find a set containing the *smallest* number of vectors that spans the space—that is, we want to find a *minimal spanning set*.

By *minimal* we mean that the set contains the smallest possible number of vectors.

The set $\{(1,0),(1,1),(1,-2)\}$ is clearly not a minimal spanning set for $\mathbb{R}^2$, since the smaller set $\{(1,0),(1,1)\}$ also spans $\mathbb{R}^2$. The vector $(1,-2)$ is redundant because it can be written as a linear combination of the vectors $(1,0)$ and $(1,1)$:

$$(1,-2) = 3(1,0) - 2(1,1).$$

Thus, if a vector (x,y) in $\mathbb{R}^2$ can be written as a linear combination of the vectors $(1,0)$, $(1,1)$ and $(1,-2)$, then it can be written as a linear combination of just the vectors $(1,0)$ and $(1,1)$:

$$\begin{aligned}
(x,y) &= \alpha(1,0) + \beta(1,1) + \gamma(1,-2) \\
&= \alpha(1,0) + \beta(1,1) + \gamma[3(1,0) - 2(1,1)] \\
&= (\alpha + 3\gamma)(1,0) + (\beta - 2\gamma)(1,1).
\end{aligned}$$

The following general result holds.

Theorem 3.1   Suppose that the vector $\mathbf{v}_k$ can be written as a linear combination of the vectors $\mathbf{v}_1, \ldots, \mathbf{v}_{k-1}$. Then the span of the set $\{\mathbf{v}_1, \mathbf{v}_2, \ldots, \mathbf{v}_k\}$ is the same as the span of the set $\{\mathbf{v}_1, \mathbf{v}_2, \ldots, \mathbf{v}_{k-1}\}$.

Proof   Let $S = \langle\{\mathbf{v}_1, \mathbf{v}_2, \ldots, \mathbf{v}_{k-1}\}\rangle$ and $T = \langle\{\mathbf{v}_1, \mathbf{v}_2, \ldots, \mathbf{v}_k\}\rangle$.

Clearly, $S \subseteq T$.

Now

$$T = \{\alpha_1\mathbf{v}_1 + \alpha_2\mathbf{v}_2 + \cdots + \alpha_k\mathbf{v}_k : \alpha_1, \alpha_2, \ldots, \alpha_k \in \mathbb{R}\}.$$

As $\mathbf{v}_k$ can be written as a linear combination of $\mathbf{v}_1, \ldots, \mathbf{v}_{k-1}$, it follows that

$$\mathbf{v}_k = \beta_1\mathbf{v}_1 + \beta_2\mathbf{v}_2 + \cdots + \beta_{k-1}\mathbf{v}_{k-1}, \text{ for some } \beta_1, \beta_2, \ldots, \beta_{k-1} \in \mathbb{R}.$$

So any element of T can be expressed in the form

$$\begin{aligned}
&\alpha_1\mathbf{v}_1 + \alpha_2\mathbf{v}_2 + \cdots + \alpha_k\mathbf{v}_k \\
&= \alpha_1\mathbf{v}_1 + \alpha_2\mathbf{v}_2 + \cdots + \alpha_{k-1}\mathbf{v}_{k-1} + \alpha_k(\beta_1\mathbf{v}_1 + \beta_2\mathbf{v}_2 + \cdots + \beta_{k-1}\mathbf{v}_{k-1}) \\
&= (\alpha_1 + \alpha_k\beta_1)\mathbf{v}_1 + (\alpha_2 + \alpha_k\beta_2)\mathbf{v}_2 + \cdots + (\alpha_{k-1} + \alpha_k\beta_{k-1})\mathbf{v}_{k-1},
\end{aligned}$$

which belongs to S. Thus $T \subseteq S$.

Combining these two results gives $S = T$, as required.   ∎

So, in order to tell whether a spanning set is minimal, we need to be able to test whether *any* vector in the set can be written as a linear combination of the remaining vectors in the set. To make this task easier, we introduce the ideas of *linear dependence* and *linear independence*.

Definitions A finite set of vectors $\{\mathbf{v}_1, \mathbf{v}_2, \ldots, \mathbf{v}_k\}$ in a vector space V is **linearly dependent** if there exist real numbers $\alpha_1, \alpha_2, \ldots, \alpha_k$, *not all zero*, such that

$$\alpha_1\mathbf{v}_1 + \alpha_2\mathbf{v}_2 + \cdots + \alpha_k\mathbf{v}_k = \mathbf{0}.$$

A finite set of vectors $\{\mathbf{v}_1, \mathbf{v}_2, \ldots, \mathbf{v}_k\}$ is **linearly independent** if it is not linearly dependent; that is, if

$$\alpha_1\mathbf{v}_1 + \alpha_2\mathbf{v}_2 + \cdots + \alpha_k\mathbf{v}_k = \mathbf{0}$$

only when $\alpha_1 = \alpha_2 = \cdots = \alpha_k = 0$.

Note that $\alpha_1 = \alpha_2 = \cdots = \alpha_k = 0$ *is* a solution to the equation whether the set of vectors is linearly dependent or linearly independent. The distinction between the two cases is whether there is a *non-zero* solution as well.

We use the term *linearly dependent* because if a set of vectors is linearly dependent, then one of them can be written as a linear combination of the others—that is, it *depends* on the others. If

$$\alpha_1\mathbf{v}_1 + \alpha_2\mathbf{v}_2 + \cdots + \alpha_k\mathbf{v}_k = \mathbf{0},$$

and α_k (for example) is non-zero, then we can rearrange the equation to give

$$\mathbf{v}_k = -\frac{\alpha_1}{\alpha_k}\mathbf{v}_1 - \cdots - \frac{\alpha_{k-1}}{\alpha_k}\mathbf{v}_{k-1},$$

For example, if $2\mathbf{v}_1 + 3\mathbf{v}_2 - 4\mathbf{v}_3 = \mathbf{0}$, then $\mathbf{v}_3 = \frac{1}{2}\mathbf{v}_1 + \frac{3}{4}\mathbf{v}_2$.

so that $\mathbf{v}_k$ is a linear combination of the remaining vectors.

Conversely, if $\mathbf{v}_k$ is a linear combination of the vectors $\mathbf{v}_1, \mathbf{v}_2, \ldots, \mathbf{v}_{k-1}$, then $\{\mathbf{v}_1, \mathbf{v}_2, \ldots, \mathbf{v}_k\}$ is a linearly dependent set.

Statements 1 to 4 below follow from the definitions.

1. If $\{\mathbf{v}_1, \mathbf{v}_2, \ldots, \mathbf{v}_k\}$ is a linearly independent set, then there is only one way in which the zero vector can be expressed as a linear combination of $\mathbf{v}_1, \mathbf{v}_2, \ldots, \mathbf{v}_k$; that is, the trivial way

   $$\mathbf{0} = 0\mathbf{v}_1 + 0\mathbf{v}_2 + \cdots + 0\mathbf{v}_k.$$

2. If $\mathbf{v}_1$ is the zero vector, then

   $$1\mathbf{v}_1 + 0\mathbf{v}_2 + \cdots + 0\mathbf{v}_k = \mathbf{0},$$

   so any set of vectors containing the zero vector is linearly dependent. It follows that *a linearly independent set cannot contain the zero vector*.

3. Any set consisting of just one non-zero vector $\mathbf{v}$ is linearly independent because if $\alpha\mathbf{v} = \mathbf{0}$, then either $\alpha = 0$ or $\mathbf{v} = \mathbf{0}$. Since $\mathbf{v}$ is non-zero, we must have $\alpha = 0$, so the set $\{\mathbf{v}\}$ is linearly independent.

4. Any set of two non-zero vectors is linearly dependent if one of the vectors is a multiple of the other, and linearly independent otherwise. For example, $\{(1, 1, 2), (2, 2, 4)\}$ is a linearly dependent set in $\mathbb{R}^3$ because

   $$(2, 2, 4) = 2(1, 1, 2),$$

   so

   $$(2, 2, 4) - 2(1, 1, 2) = (0, 0, 0),$$

   which is the zero vector in $\mathbb{R}^3$. In this case $\alpha_1 = 1$ and $\alpha_2 = -2$.

   However, $\{(1, 1, 2), (1, 2, -3)\}$ is a linearly independent set, as neither vector is a multiple of the other.

This gives us a particularly simple way of checking whether a set of two non-zero vectors is linearly dependent or linearly independent: namely, a set of two non-zero vectors is linearly independent if and only if neither vector is a multiple of the other. For vectors in $\mathbb{R}^2$ and $\mathbb{R}^3$, this is equivalent to saying that two non-zero vectors are linearly independent if and only if they do not lie along the same straight line—that is, they are not collinear.

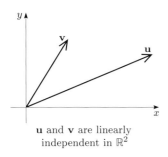

u and v are linearly
independent in $\mathbb{R}^2$

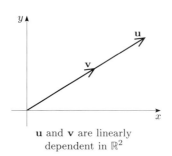

u and v are linearly
dependent in $\mathbb{R}^2$

Similarly, three non-zero vectors in $\mathbb{R}^3$ are linearly independent if and only if they do not lie in the same plane—that is, they are not coplanar.

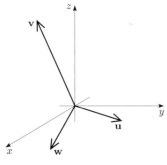

u, v and w are linearly
independent in $\mathbb{R}^3$

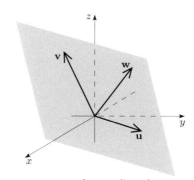

u, v and w are linearly
dependent in $\mathbb{R}^3$

More generally, we can use the following strategy to test whether a set of vectors is linearly independent.

Strategy 3.1 To test whether a given set of vectors $\{\mathbf{v}_1, \mathbf{v}_2, \ldots, \mathbf{v}_k\}$ is linearly independent.

1. Write down the equation $\alpha_1 \mathbf{v}_1 + \alpha_2 \mathbf{v}_2 + \cdots + \alpha_k \mathbf{v}_k = \mathbf{0}$.

2. Express this equation as a system of simultaneous linear equations in the unknowns $\alpha_1, \alpha_2, \ldots, \alpha_k$.

3. Solve these equations.

If the only solution is $\alpha_1 = \alpha_2 = \cdots = \alpha_k = 0$, then the set of vectors is linearly independent.

If there is a solution with at least one of $\alpha_1, \alpha_2, \ldots, \alpha_k$ not equal to zero, then the set of vectors is linearly dependent.

Example 3.1   Use Strategy 3.1 to determine whether each of the following sets of vectors in $\mathbb{R}^3$ is linearly independent.

(a) $\{(2,0,0), (0,0,1), (-1,2,1)\}$ (b) $\{(1,1,1), (0,2,1), (1,5,3)\}$

Solution   We follow the steps of Strategy 3.1.

(a) We first write $\alpha(2,0,0) + \beta(0,0,1) + \gamma(-1,2,1) = (0,0,0)$, which simplifies to   Step 1

$$(2\alpha - \gamma, 2\gamma, \beta + \gamma) = (0,0,0).$$

Equating corresponding coordinates gives the simultaneous equations   Step 2

$$\begin{cases} 2\alpha \quad - \quad \gamma = 0, \\ \qquad\quad 2\gamma = 0, \\ \quad \beta + \quad \gamma = 0. \end{cases}$$

The second equation gives $\gamma = 0$. Substituting this value into the other   Step 3
two equations gives $\alpha = 0$ and $\beta = 0$. So the equations are satisfied
only when $\alpha = \beta = \gamma = 0$, and hence this set of vectors is linearly
independent.

(b) We first write $\alpha(1,1,1) + \beta(0,2,1) + \gamma(1,5,3) = (0,0,0)$.   Step 1

Then α, β and γ satisfy the simultaneous equations   Step 2

$$\begin{cases} \alpha \qquad + \quad \gamma = 0, \\ \alpha + 2\beta + 5\gamma = 0, \\ \alpha + \quad \beta + 3\gamma = 0. \end{cases}$$

We use the method of Gauss–Jordan elimination from Unit LA2 and   Step 3
perform row-reduction on the augmented matrix below.

$$\begin{matrix} \mathbf{r}_1 \\ \mathbf{r}_2 \\ \mathbf{r}_3 \end{matrix} \qquad \left(\begin{array}{ccc|c} 1 & 0 & 1 & 0 \\ 1 & 2 & 5 & 0 \\ 1 & 1 & 3 & 0 \end{array} \right)$$

$$\begin{matrix} \\ \mathbf{r}_2 \to \mathbf{r}_2 - \mathbf{r}_1 \\ \mathbf{r}_3 \to \mathbf{r}_3 - \mathbf{r}_1 \end{matrix} \qquad \left(\begin{array}{ccc|c} 1 & 0 & 1 & 0 \\ 0 & 2 & 4 & 0 \\ 0 & 1 & 2 & 0 \end{array} \right)$$

$$\begin{matrix} \\ \mathbf{r}_2 \to \tfrac{1}{2}\mathbf{r}_2 \\ \\ \end{matrix} \qquad \left(\begin{array}{ccc|c} 1 & 0 & 1 & 0 \\ 0 & 1 & 2 & 0 \\ 0 & 1 & 2 & 0 \end{array} \right)$$

$$\begin{matrix} \\ \\ \mathbf{r}_3 \to \mathbf{r}_3 - \mathbf{r}_2 \end{matrix} \qquad \left(\begin{array}{ccc|c} 1 & 0 & 1 & 0 \\ 0 & 1 & 2 & 0 \\ 0 & 0 & 0 & 0 \end{array} \right)$$

The corresponding system of equations is

$$\begin{cases} \alpha \qquad + \quad \gamma = 0, \\ \quad \beta + 2\gamma = 0. \end{cases}$$

The solution set of the system is $\alpha = -k$, $\beta = -2k$, $\gamma = k$, $k \in \mathbb{R}$, so
there are infinitely many solutions. For example, $k = -1$ gives

$$(1,1,1) + 2(0,2,1) - (1,5,3) = (0,0,0).$$

So this set of vectors is linearly dependent. ∎

We claimed earlier that three non-zero linearly dependent vectors in $\mathbb{R}^3$ are
coplanar. In Example 3.1(b), all the vectors in the set lie in the plane
through the origin with equation $x + y - 2z = 0$.

Exercise 3.1   Determine whether each of the following sets of vectors is a linearly independent subset of V.

(a) $V = \mathbb{R}^2$, $\{(1,0),(-1,-1)\}$.

(b) $V = \mathbb{R}^2$, $\{(1,-1),(1,1),(2,1)\}$.

(c) $V = \mathbb{R}^3$, $\{(1,1,0),(-1,1,1)\}$.

(d) $V = \mathbb{R}^3$, $\{(1,0,0),(1,1,0),(1,1,1)\}$.

(e) $V = \mathbb{R}^4$, $\{(1,2,1,0),(0,-1,1,3)\}$.

Before embarking on the algebra, have a look at each set of vectors and try to decide whether you expect the set to be linearly dependent or linearly independent.

We conclude this subsection by looking briefly at linearly dependent and linearly independent sets of vectors in vector spaces other than $\mathbb{R}^2$, $\mathbb{R}^3$ and $\mathbb{R}^4$.

In the following example, we use the fact that two polynomial functions in the variable x are equal if and only if the coefficients of corresponding powers of x are equal.

Example 3.2   Determine whether the set of polynomials $\{1, 4x, 4x + x^2\}$ is a linearly independent subset of P_3.

Solution   We use Strategy 3.1.

First we write $\alpha(1) + \beta(4x) + \gamma(4x + x^2) = 0$, which can be written as

$$\alpha + (4\beta + 4\gamma)x + \gamma x^2 = 0 + 0x + 0x^2.$$

Equating the coefficients of 1, x and x^2 on each side gives

$$\begin{cases} \alpha & = 0, \\ 4\beta + 4\gamma = 0, \\ \gamma = 0. \end{cases}$$

So $\alpha = 0$, $\gamma = 0$ and, by substitution in the second equation, $\beta = 0$. Thus $\{1, 4x, 4x + x^2\}$ is a linearly independent subset of P_3. ∎

Example 3.3   Determine whether the set of matrices

$$\left\{ \begin{pmatrix} 1 & 0 \\ 0 & 2 \end{pmatrix}, \begin{pmatrix} 0 & -1 \\ -2 & 0 \end{pmatrix}, \begin{pmatrix} 2 & 1 \\ 2 & 4 \end{pmatrix} \right\}$$

is a linearly independent subset of $M_{2,2}$.

Solution   We use Strategy 3.1.

First we write

$$\alpha \begin{pmatrix} 1 & 0 \\ 0 & 2 \end{pmatrix} + \beta \begin{pmatrix} 0 & -1 \\ -2 & 0 \end{pmatrix} + \gamma \begin{pmatrix} 2 & 1 \\ 2 & 4 \end{pmatrix} = \begin{pmatrix} 0 & 0 \\ 0 & 0 \end{pmatrix},$$

which can be written as

$$\begin{pmatrix} \alpha + 2\gamma & -\beta + \gamma \\ -2\beta + 2\gamma & 2\alpha + 4\gamma \end{pmatrix} = \begin{pmatrix} 0 & 0 \\ 0 & 0 \end{pmatrix}.$$

Equating corresponding entries gives

$$\begin{cases} \alpha & + 2\gamma = 0, \\ -\beta + \gamma = 0, \\ -2\beta + 2\gamma = 0, \\ 2\alpha + 4\gamma = 0. \end{cases}$$

The third and fourth equations are multiples of the first two equations, so we need to solve only the first two. From the second equation $\beta = \gamma$, and from the first equation $\alpha = -2\gamma$.

If we choose $\gamma = 1$, then $\beta = 1$ and $\alpha = -2$; thus

$$-2 \begin{pmatrix} 1 & 0 \\ 0 & 2 \end{pmatrix} + 1 \begin{pmatrix} 0 & -1 \\ -2 & 0 \end{pmatrix} + 1 \begin{pmatrix} 2 & 1 \\ 2 & 4 \end{pmatrix} = \begin{pmatrix} 0 & 0 \\ 0 & 0 \end{pmatrix}.$$

So we can find α, β and γ not all zero such that the original equation is satisfied. So the set of matrices is linearly dependent. It is not a linearly independent subset of $M_{2,2}$. ∎

Exercise 3.2   In each of the following cases, determine whether S is a linearly independent subset of the vector space V.

(a) $V = P_4$, $S = \{1, x, x^2, x^3, 1 + x + x^2 + x^3\}$.

(b) $V = M_{2,2}$, $S = \left\{ \begin{pmatrix} 1 & 2 \\ 0 & -1 \end{pmatrix}, \begin{pmatrix} 1 & 0 \\ -1 & 2 \end{pmatrix} \right\}$.

(c) $V = \mathbb{C}$, $S = \{1 + i, 1 - i\}$.

3.2 Bases

We now use the idea of linear independence to help us find a minimal set of vectors that spans a vector space.

If we have a set of vectors that forms a spanning set for a vector space, then the set is a minimal spanning set if and only if *it is linearly independent*. This condition is certainly necessary because, as we showed in the previous subsection, if the set of vectors is linearly dependent, then we can write at least one of the vectors as a linear combination of the other vectors. Such a vector is redundant, and we can drop it from the set, so the set is not a minimal set.

The condition is also sufficient. Let $S = \{\mathbf{v}_1, \mathbf{v}_2, \ldots, \mathbf{v}_k\}$ be a linearly independent spanning set for a vector space V, and suppose that the set $S_1 = \{\mathbf{v}_1, \ldots, \mathbf{v}_{k-1}\}$ also spans V. Then we can write

We give a proof by contradiction.

$$\mathbf{v}_k = \alpha_1 \mathbf{v}_1 + \cdots + \alpha_{k-1} \mathbf{v}_{k-1},$$

for some $\alpha_1, \ldots, \alpha_{k-1}$ not all equal to 0. Therefore

$$\alpha_1 \mathbf{v}_1 + \cdots + \alpha_{k-1} \mathbf{v}_{k-1} - \mathbf{v}_k = \mathbf{0},$$

so S is not linearly independent. But this is a contradiction, so our initial assumption that S_1 spans V must be wrong. Thus S_1 cannot span V.

If we have a linearly independent set of vectors that spans a vector space, then we give the set of vectors a special name.

Definition   A **basis** for a vector space V is a linearly independent set of vectors which is a spanning set for V.

For example, $\{(1,1), (-1,2)\}$ is a spanning set for $\mathbb{R}^2$. Since it is also a linearly independent set, it is a basis for $\mathbb{R}^2$. Although the set $\{(1,0), (1,1), (1,-2)\}$ is also a spanning set for $\mathbb{R}^2$, it is not linearly independent, as we showed earlier in this section, so it is not a basis for $\mathbb{R}^2$.

Exercise 2.5

While each vector in $\mathbb{R}^2$ can be written as a linear combination of vectors in the spanning set $\{(1,0), (1,1), (1,-2)\}$, this expression is not unique.

For example,

$$(0,1) = 2(1,0) - 1(1,1) - 1(1,-2)$$
$$= -4(1,0) + 3(1,1) + 1(1,-2).$$

An important property of a basis for a vector space V is that each vector in V has a *unique* expression as a linear combination of basis vectors.

Theorem 3.2   Let S be a basis for a vector space V. Then each vector in V can be expressed as a linear combination of the vectors in S in only one way.

Proof   Let $S = \{\mathbf{v}_1, \mathbf{v}_2, \ldots, \mathbf{v}_k\}$ be a basis for a vector space V. We assume that a vector in V can be written as a linear combination of $\mathbf{v}_1, \mathbf{v}_2, \ldots, \mathbf{v}_k$ in two different ways, and show that this leads to a contradiction.

Let $\mathbf{u}$ be a vector in V, and assume that we can write $\mathbf{u}$ as a linear combination of the vectors in S in two different ways as:

$$\mathbf{u} = \alpha_1 \mathbf{v}_1 + \alpha_2 \mathbf{v}_2 + \cdots + \alpha_k \mathbf{v}_k$$

and

$$\mathbf{u} = \beta_1 \mathbf{v}_1 + \beta_2 \mathbf{v}_2 + \cdots + \beta_k \mathbf{v}_k.$$

Then

$$\mathbf{0} = \mathbf{u} - \mathbf{u} = (\alpha_1 - \beta_1)\mathbf{v}_1 + (\alpha_2 - \beta_2)\mathbf{v}_2 + \cdots + (\alpha_k - \beta_k)\mathbf{v}_k,$$

and $(\alpha_1 - \beta_1), (\alpha_2 - \beta_2), \ldots, (\alpha_k - \beta_k)$ are not all zero.

Therefore the set S is linearly dependent. But S is a basis for V, and is therefore linearly independent. This contradiction shows that Theorem 3.2 is true.   ∎

The definition of a basis gives us a strategy for testing whether a given set of vectors is a basis for a particular vector space.

Strategy 3.2 To determine whether a set of vectors S in a vector space V is a basis for V, check the following conditions.

(1) S is linearly independent.

(2) S spans V.

If both (1) and (2) hold, then S is a basis for V.

If either (1) or (2) does not hold, then S is not a basis for V.

Example 3.4   Show that $S = \{(2,0,2), (1,1,1), (0,1,-1)\}$ is a basis for $\mathbb{R}^3$.

Solution   We check both conditions in Strategy 3.2.

Suppose that   Condition (1)

$$\alpha(2,0,2) + \beta(1,1,1) + \gamma(0,1,-1) = (0,0,0),$$

that is,

$$(2\alpha + \beta, \beta + \gamma, 2\alpha + \beta - \gamma) = (0,0,0).$$

Equating corresponding coordinates, we obtain the simultaneous equations

$$\begin{cases} 2\alpha + \beta && = 0, \\ & \beta + \gamma = 0, \\ 2\alpha + \beta - \gamma = 0. \end{cases}$$

Subtracting the third equation from the first gives $\gamma = 0$, and substituting this into the second equation gives $\beta = 0$. Finally, substituting $\beta = 0$ into the first equation gives $\alpha = 0$, so the set S is linearly independent.

We check whether each vector in $\mathbb{R}^3$ can be written as a linear combination of the vectors in the set. Choosing (x, y, z) as an arbitrary vector in $\mathbb{R}^3$, we seek numbers α, β and γ such that

$$(x, y, z) = \alpha(2, 0, 2) + \beta(1, 1, 1) + \gamma(0, 1, -1).$$

We could also use Gauss–Jordan elimination to solve this set of equations.

Condition (2)

Equating corresponding coordinates, we obtain the simultaneous equations

$$\begin{cases} 2\alpha + \beta && = x, \\ & \beta + \gamma = y, \\ 2\alpha + \beta - \gamma = z. \end{cases}$$

Subtracting the third equation from the first gives $\gamma = x - z$, and substituting this into the second equation gives $\beta = y - x + z$. Finally, substituting for β in the first equation gives $\alpha = \frac{1}{2}(2x - y - z)$. So

$$\begin{aligned}(x, y, z) = &\tfrac{1}{2}(2x - y - z)(2, 0, 2) + (y - x + z)(1, 1, 1) \\ &+ (x - z)(0, 1, -1),\end{aligned}$$

and the set of vectors S spans $\mathbb{R}^3$.

Since conditions (1) and (2) hold, the set S is a basis for $\mathbb{R}^3$. ∎

Example 3.5   Determine whether each of the following sets is a basis for $\mathbb{R}^3$.

(a) $\{(0, 1, 2), (1, 2, -1)\}$ (b) $\{(1, 1, 1), (0, 2, 1), (1, 5, 3)\}$

Solution

(a) The set $\{(0, 1, 2), (1, 2, -1)\}$ is linearly independent, as the second vector is not a multiple of the first.

   To check whether it is a spanning set for $\mathbb{R}^3$, we check whether each vector in $\mathbb{R}^3$ can be written as a linear combination of the vectors in the set. Choosing (x, y, z) as an arbitrary vector in $\mathbb{R}^3$, we seek numbers α and β such that

   $$(x, y, z) = \alpha(0, 1, 2) + \beta(1, 2, -1).$$

   Equating corresponding coordinates gives

   $$\begin{cases} && \beta = x, \\ \alpha &+ 2\beta = y, \\ 2\alpha &- \beta = z. \end{cases}$$

   Substituting $\beta = x$ from the first equation into the other two equations gives

   $$\begin{cases} \alpha = y - 2x, \\ \alpha = \tfrac{1}{2}(x + z). \end{cases}$$

   These equations are true simultaneously if and only if $y - 2x = \frac{1}{2}(x + z)$; that is, if and only if $5x - 2y + z = 0$.

This shows that $\langle\{(0, 1, 2), (1, 2, -1)\}\rangle$ is the plane $5x - 2y + z = 0$ in $\mathbb{R}^3$.

This contradicts the assumption that x, y and z can take any real values, so $\{(0, 1, 2), (1, 2, -1)\}$ is not a spanning set for $\mathbb{R}^3$. Thus it is not a basis for $\mathbb{R}^3$.

(b) The set $\{(1, 1, 1), (0, 2, 1), (1, 5, 3)\}$ is linearly dependent (see Example 3.1(b)), so it is not a basis for $\mathbb{R}^3$.   ■

Exercise 3.3 Determine whether each of the following sets is a basis for $\mathbb{R}^3$.

(a) $\{(0, 1, 2), (0, 2, 3), (0, 6, 1)\}$

(b) $\{(1, 2, 1), (1, 0, -1), (0, 3, 1)\}$

(c) $\{(1, 0, 0), (0, 1, 0), (0, 0, 1), (1, 1, 1)\}$

Exercise 3.4 Determine whether $\{(1, 2, -1, -1), (-1, 5, 1, 3)\}$ is a basis for $\mathbb{R}^4$.

We now consider bases for vector spaces other than $\mathbb{R}^2$, $\mathbb{R}^3$ and $\mathbb{R}^4$.

Example 3.6   Determine whether each of the following sets is a basis for P_3.

(a) $\{1, x, x^2\}$ (b) $\{1, x\}$ (c) $\{1, 2 + x^2, x^2\}$

Solution

(a) We need to check whether $\{1, x, x^2\}$ is linearly independent and spans P_3. To check whether the set is linearly independent, let

$$\alpha 1 + \beta x + \gamma x^2 = 0 + 0x + 0x^2.$$

Comparing coefficients of 1, x and x^2, we have $\alpha = \beta = \gamma = 0$ as the only solution; so the set is linearly independent.

To check whether it spans P_3, take a typical polynomial $a + bx + cx^2$ in P_3. Then

$$a + bx + cx^2 = a(1) + b(x) + c(x^2),$$

so $\{1, x, x^2\}$ spans P_3. Thus $\{1, x, x^2\}$ is a basis for P_3.

(b) The set $\{1, x\}$ is linearly independent, but it does not span P_3: for example, x^2 cannot be expressed as a linear combination of 1 and x. The span of this set consists of polynomials of the form $a + bx$, which is a proper subset of P_3.

(c) The set $\{1, 2 + x^2, x^2\}$ is not linearly independent, since

$$2 + x^2 = 2(1) + 1(x^2).$$

So $\{1, 2 + x^2, x^2\}$ is not a basis for P_3. The span of this set consists of all polynomials of the form $a + bx^2$.   ■

Proper subsets are defined in Unit I2, Section 1.

Exercise 3.5 Determine whether

$$S = \left\{ \begin{pmatrix} 1 & 0 \\ 1 & 0 \end{pmatrix}, \begin{pmatrix} 0 & -1 \\ 1 & 0 \end{pmatrix}, \begin{pmatrix} 2 & 0 \\ 0 & 1 \end{pmatrix}, \begin{pmatrix} -3 & 1 \\ 0 & 0 \end{pmatrix} \right\}$$

is a basis for $M_{2,2}$.

3.3 Standard bases

In working through the examples and exercises in the previous subsection, you may have noticed that we often use a particularly simple set of basis vectors for each vector space. For $\mathbb{R}^2$ this set is $\{(1,0),(0,1)\}$, for $\mathbb{R}^3$ it is $\{(1,0,0),(0,1,0),(0,0,1)\}$, for $\mathbb{R}^4$ it is $\{(1,0,0,0),(0,1,0,0),(0,0,1,0),(0,0,0,1)\}$, and so on.

The representation of a vector in terms of these bases is particularly simple. For example, in $\mathbb{R}^2$

$$(x,y) = x(1,0) + y(0,1),$$

and in $\mathbb{R}^3$

$$(x,y,z) = x(1,0,0) + y(0,1,0) + z(0,0,1).$$

Because these bases are so simple, they are used frequently; they are called *standard bases*.

Definition   The **standard basis** for $\mathbb{R}^n$ is the set of n vectors

$$\{(1,0,\ldots,0),(0,1,\ldots,0),\ldots,(0,0,\ldots,1)\}.$$

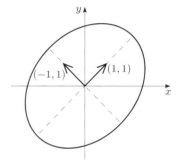

The standard basis for $\mathbb{R}^n$ seems so natural that you may wonder why we do not use it all the time. In some physical situations, however, we may need to choose a different basis. For example, if we are looking at an ellipse centred at the origin, we may want to choose basis vectors along the major and minor axes of the ellipse. For the ellipse shown in the margin, it may be more convenient to choose the basis vectors $(1,1)$ and $(-1,1)$ rather than the standard ones, $(1,0)$ and $(0,1)$. Similarly, if we are considering a parallelogram, we may want to choose basis vectors along the sides of the parallelogram.

In many vector spaces other than $\mathbb{R}^n$ there are particularly simple bases which we call the standard bases for these spaces. Here are some examples.

$$P_n: \quad \{1,x,x^2,\ldots,x^{n-1}\}$$

$$M_{2,2}: \quad \left\{ \begin{pmatrix} 1 & 0 \\ 0 & 0 \end{pmatrix}, \begin{pmatrix} 0 & 1 \\ 0 & 0 \end{pmatrix}, \begin{pmatrix} 0 & 0 \\ 1 & 0 \end{pmatrix}, \begin{pmatrix} 0 & 0 \\ 0 & 1 \end{pmatrix} \right\}$$

$$\mathbb{C}: \quad \{1,i\}$$

We met the standard basis for P_3 earlier in the section.

If we write a vector in $\mathbb{R}^2$ as (x,y), then x and y are the coordinates of the vector with respect to the standard basis vectors—that is,

$$(x,y) = x(1,0) + y(0,1).$$

However, we need some way of indicating what the coordinates of a vector are with respect to non-standard basis vectors. We use the following notation.

> **Definitions**   Let $E = \{\mathbf{e}_1, \mathbf{e}_2, \ldots, \mathbf{e}_n\}$ be a basis for a vector space V, and suppose that
>
> $$\mathbf{v} = v_1\mathbf{e}_1 + v_2\mathbf{e}_2 + \cdots + v_n\mathbf{e}_n,$$
>
> where $v_1, \ldots, v_n \in \mathbb{R}$.
>
> Then the **E-coordinate representation** of $\mathbf{v}$ is
>
> $$\mathbf{v}_E = (v_1, v_2, \ldots, v_n)_E.$$
>
> We call $v_1, \ldots, v_n$ the coordinates of $\mathbf{v}$ with respect to the basis E, or, more briefly, the **E-coordinates** of $\mathbf{v}$.

We usually omit the subscript if E is the standard basis.

We shall use this notation frequently in Unit LA4.

Remarks

1. We have introduced the alternative notation $E = \{\mathbf{e}_1, \mathbf{e}_2, \ldots, \mathbf{e}_n\}$ for a basis in order to avoid confusion between vectors $\mathbf{v}_1, \mathbf{v}_2, \ldots, \mathbf{v}_n$ and coordinates $v_1, \ldots, v_n$ of a vector $\mathbf{v}$. The E-coordinates of a vector $\mathbf{v}_j$ will be denoted by $v_{1j}, v_{2j}, \ldots, v_{nj}$. So we write $\mathbf{v}_j = \displaystyle\sum_{i=1}^{n} v_{ij}\mathbf{e}_i$.

2. Since E is a basis for V, the E-coordinate representation of a vector in V is unique. Note that the order of the coordinates in such a representation depends on the order of the basis vectors.

3. A non-zero vector has a different coordinate representation for each different basis. For the zero vector, the coordinates are always zero.

4. If E is a standard basis, then we refer to the *standard coordinate representation*, *standard coordinates*, and so on.

The different representations of a vector are analogous to the same amount of money being expressed in different currencies.

The following examples show this notation in practice.

Example 3.7   Let $E = \{(-1, 2), (2, 2)\}$ be a basis for $\mathbb{R}^2$. Determine the standard coordinate representation of $(3, 2)_E$.

Solution   Since the vector has E-coordinates $(3, 2)_E$, its standard coordinates are obtained as follows.

$$(3, 2)_E = 3(-1, 2) + 2(2, 2) = (-3, 6) + (4, 4) = (1, 10) \quad \blacksquare$$

Exercise 3.6

(a) Let $E = \{(1, 2), (-3, 1)\}$ be a basis for $\mathbb{R}^2$. Determine the standard coordinate representation of $(2, 1)_E$.

(b) Let $E = \{(1, 0, 2), (-1, 1, 3), (2, -2, 0)\}$ be a basis for $\mathbb{R}^3$. Determine the standard coordinate representation of $(1, 1, -1)_E$.

We can also turn the method in Example 3.7 around to express a given vector in terms of a non-standard basis.

Example 3.8   For each of the following bases E for $\mathbb{R}^2$, find the E-coordinate representation of the vector $(1, 4)$.

(a) $E = \{(1, 4), (4, -1)\}$ (b) $E = \{(-1, 2), (2, 2)\}$

Solution

(a) We write $(1,4) = \alpha(1,4) + \beta(4,-1)$, which clearly has the solution $\alpha = 1$, $\beta = 0$, so

$$(1,4) = 1(1,4) + 0(4,-1) = (1,0)_E.$$

(b) We write $(1,4) = \alpha(-1,2) + \beta(2,2) = (-\alpha + 2\beta, 2\alpha + 2\beta)$.

This gives the simultaneous equations

$$\begin{cases} -\alpha + 2\beta = 1, \\ 2\alpha + 2\beta = 4. \end{cases}$$

Solving these equations gives $\alpha = 1$ and $\beta = 1$, so

$$(1,4) = 1(-1,2) + 1(2,2) = (1,1)_E. \quad \blacksquare$$

Geometrically, we are changing the axes: for part (b), see the diagram below.

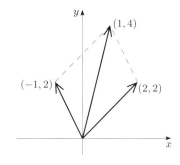

Example 3.9   Find the E-coordinate representation of the vector $(-2,0,1)$ with respect to the basis $E = \{(1,0,0), (1,0,1), (2,1,-1)\}$ for $\mathbb{R}^3$.

Solution   We write

$$\begin{aligned} (-2,0,1) &= \alpha(1,0,0) + \beta(1,0,1) + \gamma(2,1,-1) \\ &= (\alpha + \beta + 2\gamma, \gamma, \beta - \gamma). \end{aligned}$$

This gives the simultaneous equations

$$\begin{cases} \alpha + \beta + 2\gamma = -2, \\ \gamma = 0, \\ \beta - \gamma = 1. \end{cases}$$

The second equation gives $\gamma = 0$. Substituting this value into the third equation gives $\beta = 1$, and substituting these values into the first equation gives $\alpha = -3$. So

$$(-2,0,1) = -3(1,0,0) + 1(1,0,1) + 0(2,1,-1) = (-3,1,0)_E. \quad \blacksquare$$

Exercise 3.7

(a) Find the E-coordinate representation of the vector $(5,-4)$ with respect to the basis $E = \{(1,2), (-3,1)\}$ for $\mathbb{R}^2$.

(b) Find the E-coordinate representation of the vector $(-3,5,7)$ with respect to the basis $E = \{(1,0,2), (-1,1,3), (2,-2,0)\}$ for $\mathbb{R}^3$.

3.4 Dimension

From your work in Unit LA1 you should have gained an intuitive idea of dimension in geometry—namely that $\mathbb{R}$ is one-dimensional, $\mathbb{R}^2$ is two-dimensional, and so on. You may also have noticed in the previous subsection that all the bases you met for $\mathbb{R}^2$ contained two vectors, all the bases for $\mathbb{R}^3$ contained three vectors, and so on. For example, among the bases you met were the following.

$\mathbb{R}^2$: $\{(1,0), (0,1)\}$, $\{(1,0), (1,1)\}$, $\{(1,2), (-1,1)\}$.

$\mathbb{R}^3$: $\{(1,0,0), (0,1,0), (0,0,1)\}$, $\{(1,2,1), (1,0,-1), (0,3,1)\}$.

$\mathbb{R}^4$: $\{(1,0,2,0), (0,1,0,3), (0,0,1,2), (2,0,-1,0)\}$,

$\quad \{(1,0,0,0), (0,1,0,0), (0,0,1,0), (0,0,0,1)\}$.

It is not a coincidence that every basis for $\mathbb{R}^2$ contains exactly two vectors, and every basis for $\mathbb{R}^3$ contains exactly three vectors.

The main theorem in this section, the *Basis Theorem*, states that if V is any vector space, then *every basis for V contains the same number of vectors*. Before we prove this, we must define what we mean by a finite-dimensional vector space.

Definitions Let V be a vector space. Then V is **finite dimensional** if it contains a finite set of vectors S which forms a basis for V. If no such set exists, then V is **infinite dimensional**.

Examples of infinite-dimensional vector spaces are $\mathbb{R}^\infty$ and the set of polynomials of any degree.

In order to prove that every basis for a finite-dimensional vector space V contains the same number of vectors, we first prove the following useful result.

Theorem 3.3 Let $E = \{\mathbf{e}_1, \mathbf{e}_2, \ldots, \mathbf{e}_n\}$ be a basis for a vector space V, and let $S = \{\mathbf{v}_1, \mathbf{v}_2, \ldots, \mathbf{v}_m\}$ be a set of m vectors in V, where $m > n$. Then S is a linearly dependent set.

Proof   Assume that the conditions of Theorem 3.3 hold. We want to show that S is linearly dependent. Since E is a basis, each of the vectors $\mathbf{v}_1, \mathbf{v}_2, \ldots, \mathbf{v}_m$ can be written as a linear combination of the vectors in E; that is,

$$\mathbf{v}_1 = v_{11}\mathbf{e}_1 + v_{21}\mathbf{e}_2 + \cdots + v_{n1}\mathbf{e}_n,$$
$$\mathbf{v}_2 = v_{12}\mathbf{e}_1 + v_{22}\mathbf{e}_2 + \cdots + v_{n2}\mathbf{e}_n,$$
$$\vdots$$
$$\mathbf{v}_m = v_{1m}\mathbf{e}_1 + v_{2m}\mathbf{e}_2 + \cdots + v_{nm}\mathbf{e}_n,$$

for some numbers $v_{11}, \ldots, v_{nm} \in \mathbb{R}$.

To show that S is linearly dependent, we must find real numbers $\alpha_1, \alpha_2, \ldots, \alpha_m$, not all zero, such that

$$\alpha_1 \mathbf{v}_1 + \alpha_2 \mathbf{v}_2 + \cdots + \alpha_m \mathbf{v}_m = \mathbf{0}. \tag{3.1}$$

Using the first set of equations, we can rewrite equation (3.1) as

$$(\alpha_1 v_{11} + \alpha_2 v_{12} + \cdots + \alpha_m v_{1m})\mathbf{e}_1$$
$$+ (\alpha_1 v_{21} + \alpha_2 v_{22} + \cdots + \alpha_m v_{2m})\mathbf{e}_2$$
$$+ \cdots + (\alpha_1 v_{n1} + \alpha_2 v_{n2} + \cdots + \alpha_m v_{nm})\mathbf{e}_n = \mathbf{0}. \tag{3.2}$$

Since E is a basis, the set of vectors $\{\mathbf{e}_1, \mathbf{e}_2, \ldots, \mathbf{e}_n\}$ is linearly independent, so equation (3.2) is satisfied if and only if the following set of equations has a non-zero solution for $\alpha_1, \alpha_2, \ldots, \alpha_m$:

$$\begin{cases} v_{11}\alpha_1 + v_{12}\alpha_2 + \cdots + v_{1m}\alpha_m = 0, \\ v_{21}\alpha_1 + v_{22}\alpha_2 + \cdots + v_{2m}\alpha_m = 0, \\ \qquad\qquad \vdots \\ v_{n1}\alpha_1 + v_{n2}\alpha_2 + \cdots + v_{nm}\alpha_m = 0. \end{cases}$$

This is a system of n linear equations in m unknowns with $m > n$, so there are more unknowns than equations. In Unit LA2 we showed that such a system of equations has a non-trivial solution—that is, a solution for which some variables are non-zero. So the set S containing $m > n$ vectors is linearly dependent. This proves the theorem. ∎

If you are short of time, omit the proof.

Unit LA2, Section 1.

For example, $\mathbb{R}^3$ has three vectors in its standard basis, so, by Theorem 3.3, the set

$$\{(1,1,0),(0,-2,1),(0,0,1),(1,1,2)\}$$

is linearly dependent because it contains more than three vectors. So

$$(1,1,0)+0(0,-2,1)+2(0,0,1)-(1,1,2)=(0,0,0).$$

Theorem 3.3 has the following immediate, and useful, consequence.

Corollary to Theorem 3.3   Let V be a vector space with a basis containing n vectors. If a linearly independent subset of V contains m vectors, then $m \le n$.

This corollary provides the crucial steps in the proof of the Basis Theorem.

Theorem 3.4 Basis Theorem

Let V be a finite-dimensional vector space. Then every basis for V contains the same number of vectors.

Proof   Let $\{\mathbf{e}_1,\mathbf{e}_2,\ldots,\mathbf{e}_n\}$ and $\{\mathbf{f}_1,\mathbf{f}_2,\ldots,\mathbf{f}_m\}$ be two bases for a finite-dimensional vector space V. We shall prove that $n=m$.

Since $\{\mathbf{e}_1,\mathbf{e}_2,\ldots,\mathbf{e}_n\}$ is a basis for V and $\{\mathbf{f}_1,\mathbf{f}_2,\ldots,\mathbf{f}_m\}$ is a linearly independent set, we have $m \le n$, by the corollary to Theorem 3.3.

Similarly, since $\{\mathbf{f}_1,\mathbf{f}_2,\ldots,\mathbf{f}_m\}$ is a basis for V and $\{\mathbf{e}_1,\mathbf{e}_2,\ldots,\mathbf{e}_n\}$ is linearly independent, we have $n \le m$, by the corollary to Theorem 3.3.

Therefore $m=n$, so every basis contains the same number of vectors.   ∎

The Basis Theorem allows us to give a definition of the dimension of a finite-dimensional vector space which agrees with our intuitive geometric idea of dimension.

Definition   The **dimension** of a finite-dimensional vector space V, denoted by $\dim V$, is the number of vectors in any basis for the space.

So $\mathbb{R}^2$ has dimension 2 and $\mathbb{R}^3$ has dimension 3, as we expected from the geometry. More generally, $\mathbb{R}^n$ has dimension n, since the standard basis for $\mathbb{R}^n$ has n vectors. It follows from Theorem 3.4 that every basis for $\mathbb{R}^n$ contains exactly n vectors. The strategy for checking whether a set of vectors is a basis (Strategy 3.2) can now be greatly simplified when the vector space is $\mathbb{R}^n$. The result that we need is stated in the next theorem.

Theorem 3.5   Let V be an n-dimensional vector space. Then any set of n linearly independent vectors in V is a basis for V.

Proof   Suppose that the set $S = \{\mathbf{v}_1, \mathbf{v}_2, \ldots, \mathbf{v}_n\}$ of n linearly independent vectors does not span V. Then there exists a vector $\mathbf{v}$ in V that cannot be written as a linear combination of the vectors in S. Hence $\{\mathbf{v}_1, \mathbf{v}_2, \ldots, \mathbf{v}_n, \mathbf{v}\}$ is a linearly independent set of vectors.

We give a proof by contradiction.

Indeed, if

$$\alpha_1 \mathbf{v}_1 + \cdots + \alpha_n \mathbf{v}_n + \alpha_{n+1} \mathbf{v} = \mathbf{0},$$

then $\alpha_{n+1} = 0$, since $\mathbf{v}$ cannot be written as a linear combination of the vectors in S and $\alpha_1 = \ldots = \alpha_n = 0$, since S is linearly independent.

But by Theorem 3.3, any set of more than n vectors is linearly dependent. This is a contradiction, so the original statement must be false, so S does span V.

Therefore every set of n linearly independent vectors in V is a basis for V.   ∎

This means that to check whether a set S is a basis for $\mathbb{R}^n$, we no longer have to check that S spans $\mathbb{R}^n$. We have the following simplified strategy.

Strategy 3.3   To determine whether a set of vectors S in $\mathbb{R}^n$ is a basis for the vector space $\mathbb{R}^n$, check the following conditions.

(1) S contains n vectors.

(2) S is linearly independent.

If both (1) and (2) hold, then S is a basis for $\mathbb{R}^n$.

If either (1) or (2) does not hold, then S is not a basis for $\mathbb{R}^n$.

We can use a similar strategy to determine whether a set of vectors is a basis for any vector space V *if* we know the dimension of V.

Exercise 3.8   Use Strategy 3.3 to determine which of the following sets is a basis for $\mathbb{R}^3$.

(a) $\{(1, 2, 1), (1, 0, -1)\}$

(b) $\{(1, 2, 1), (1, 0, -1), (0, 3, 1)\}$

(c) $\{(1, -1, 0), (2, 1, 4), (3, 0, 4)\}$

(d) $\{(1, 0, 0), (0, 1, 0), (0, 0, 1), (1, 1, 1)\}$

You may have noticed that some of the parts of Exercise 3.8 appeared in earlier exercises as well. This time you should have found them much easier to do, since you can eliminate some of the sets because they do not contain the right number of vectors, and you do not need to check spanning, which is usually harder than checking for linear independence.

Next we look at the dimensions of various other vector spaces.

In Subsection 3.3 we listed the standard bases for some vector spaces as follows.

$\mathbb{R}^n$: $\{(1, 0, \ldots, 0), (0, 1, \ldots, 0), \ldots, (0, 0, \ldots, 1)\}$.

P_n: $\{1, x, x^2, \ldots, x^{n-1}\}$.

$M_{2,2}$: $\left\{ \begin{pmatrix} 1 & 0 \\ 0 & 0 \end{pmatrix}, \begin{pmatrix} 0 & 1 \\ 0 & 0 \end{pmatrix}, \begin{pmatrix} 0 & 0 \\ 1 & 0 \end{pmatrix}, \begin{pmatrix} 0 & 0 \\ 0 & 1 \end{pmatrix} \right\}$.

$\mathbb{C}$: $\{1, i\}$.

We can see that the dimension of P_n is n, so the dimension of P_2 is 2, the dimension of P_3 is 3, and so on.

Similarly, the dimension of $M_{2,2}$ is 4, and, in general, the dimension of $M_{m,n}$ is mn. For example, $M_{2,3}$ has dimension 6: a basis is

$$\left\{ \begin{pmatrix} 1 & 0 & 0 \\ 0 & 0 & 0 \end{pmatrix}, \begin{pmatrix} 0 & 1 & 0 \\ 0 & 0 & 0 \end{pmatrix}, \begin{pmatrix} 0 & 0 & 1 \\ 0 & 0 & 0 \end{pmatrix}, \right.$$
$$\left. \begin{pmatrix} 0 & 0 & 0 \\ 1 & 0 & 0 \end{pmatrix}, \begin{pmatrix} 0 & 0 & 0 \\ 0 & 1 & 0 \end{pmatrix}, \begin{pmatrix} 0 & 0 & 0 \\ 0 & 0 & 1 \end{pmatrix} \right\}.$$

Finally, the dimension of $\mathbb{C}$ is 2.

We end this section by showing that a linearly independent subset of a vector space can always be extended to a basis for the vector space.

We use this result in Unit LA4, Section 4.

Theorem 3.6   Let $S = \{\mathbf{v}_1, \mathbf{v}_2, \ldots, \mathbf{v}_m\}$ be a linearly independent subset of an n-dimensional vector space V, where $m < n$. Then there exist vectors $\mathbf{v}_{m+1}, \ldots, \mathbf{v}_n$ in V such that $\{\mathbf{v}_1, \mathbf{v}_2, \ldots, \mathbf{v}_n\}$ is a basis for V.

Proof   Since $m < n$, S is not a basis for V, by the Basis Theorem. Thus there is a vector $\mathbf{v}_{m+1}$ in V that cannot be expressed as a linear combination of the vectors in S. As in the proof of Theorem 3.5, it follows that $\{\mathbf{v}_1, \mathbf{v}_2, \ldots, \mathbf{v}_{m+1}\}$ is linearly independent.

We keep adding vectors in this way until we obtain a linearly independent set with n vectors. This is a basis, by Theorem 3.5.   ∎

Further exercises

Exercise 3.9   Determine which of the following sets are linearly independent.

(a) $\{(0,0), (1,1)\}$ in $\mathbb{R}^2$.

(b) $\{(1,1,0), (1,0,1), (0,1,1)\}$ in $\mathbb{R}^3$.

(c) $\{1 + 2x, 3x, 2 - 4x\}$ in P_2.

Exercise 3.10   Determine in each of the following cases whether the set S is a basis for the vector space V.

(a) $V = \mathbb{R}^2$, $S = \{(\frac{1}{2}, 2), (2, \frac{1}{2})\}$.

(b) $V = \mathbb{R}^3$, $S = \{(1,2,-3), (4,7,-5)\}$.

(c) $V - \mathbb{R}^4$, $S - \{(1,0,0,0), (1,1,0,0), (1,1,1,0), (1,1,1,1)\}$.

Exercise 3.11   By testing for linear independence and spanning, determine in each case whether the set S is a basis for the vector space V.

(a) $V = M_{2,1}$, $S = \left\{ \begin{pmatrix} 1 \\ 2 \end{pmatrix}, \begin{pmatrix} 1 \\ 4 \end{pmatrix} \right\}$.

(b) $V = P_3$, $S = \{2 + x, 3 - x^2\}$.

(c) $V = \mathbb{C}$, $S = \{1 - 2i, 2 - 4i\}$.

Exercise 3.12   Classify each of the following statements as true or false.

(a) Any set of vectors containing the zero vector $\mathbf{0}$ is linearly dependent.

(b) In $\mathbb{R}^3$, a set of four vectors can be found which is linearly independent.

(c) In $\mathbb{R}^n$, any set of m vectors, where $m > n$, is linearly dependent.

(d) Any basis consists of linearly independent vectors.

(e) Any basis for a vector space V spans V.

(f) Any set of vectors that spans $\mathbb{R}^n$ is a basis for $\mathbb{R}^n$.

(g) Any linearly independent set of vectors in a vector space V is a basis for V.

(h) Any linearly independent spanning set of $\mathbb{R}^n$ is a basis for $\mathbb{R}^n$.

(i) Any vector in a linearly independent set can be expressed as a linear combination of the other vectors.

4   Subspaces

After working through this section, you should be able to:

(a) explain what is meant by a *subspace* of a vector space;

(b) test whether a given subset of a vector space is a subspace;

(c) find a basis for a subspace, and hence find its dimension.

4.1 Definition

During our study of spanning sets in Section 2, we came across examples in which a set of vectors does not span the whole of a vector space, but spans only a proper subset of that vector space. In particular, you saw the following.

Example 2.8 and Exercise 2.8.

- In $\mathbb{R}^2$, the set of vectors $\{(1,1)\}$ is a spanning set for the line through the origin with equation $y = x$; this is a one-dimensional subset of $\mathbb{R}^2$.
- In $\mathbb{R}^3$, the set of vectors $\{(1,0,0)\}$ is a spanning set for the x-axis; this is a one-dimensional subset of $\mathbb{R}^3$.
- In $\mathbb{R}^3$, the set of vectors $\{(1,0,1),(2,0,3)\}$ is a spanning set for the plane $y = 0$; this is a two-dimensional subset of $\mathbb{R}^3$.

In fact, any proper subset of $\mathbb{R}^3$ which is the span of a set of vectors must be $\{\mathbf{0}\}$, or a line through the origin (a one-dimensional subset), or a plane through the origin (a two-dimensional subset).

When you met these examples, you may have asked yourself whether these subsets are themselves vector spaces. In fact, they are; we call such subsets *subspaces*.

Definition   A subset S of a vector space V is a **subspace** of V if S is itself a vector space under vector addition and scalar multiplication as defined in V.

In order to prove that a subset S is a vector space, we must show that it satisfies all the axioms in Section 1. In practice, however, we do not need

See page 10.

to check them all, as many of them carry over from V; that is, if they are true for V, then they are also true for S. For example, A5 states that $\mathbf{v}_1 + \mathbf{v}_2 = \mathbf{v}_2 + \mathbf{v}_1$, for all $\mathbf{v}_1, \mathbf{v}_2 \in V$; since all the vectors in S are also in V, this property holds for S.

Provided that S is non-empty, the only axioms that need to be checked are A1 and S1. We state this in the following theorem, leaving the proof as an exercise.

We can replace the condition that S is non-empty by the condition that the zero vector is in S.

Theorem 4.1   A subset S of a vector space V is a subspace of V if it satisfies the following conditions.

(a) $\mathbf{0} \in S$.

(b) S is closed under vector addition.

(c) S is closed under scalar multiplication.

This theorem allows us to give a strategy for testing whether a given subset of a vector space is a subspace.

Strategy 4.1   To test whether a given subset S of a vector space V is a subspace of V, check the following conditions.

(1) $\mathbf{0} \in S$ (zero vector).

(2) If $\mathbf{v}_1, \mathbf{v}_2 \in S$, then $\mathbf{v}_1 + \mathbf{v}_2 \in S$ (vector addition).

(3) If $\mathbf{v} \in S$ and $\alpha \in \mathbb{R}$, then $\alpha\mathbf{v} \in S$ (scalar multiplication).

If (1), (2) and (3) hold, then S is a subspace of V.

If any of (1), (2) or (3) does not hold, then S is not a subspace of V.

The following examples show how this strategy is used.

Example 4.1   Show that the set of vectors $S = \{(x, 3x) : x \in \mathbb{R}\}$ is a subspace of $\mathbb{R}^2$.

Solution   We use Strategy 4.1.

S contains the zero vector of $\mathbb{R}^2$: if $x = 0$, then $(x, 3x) = (0, 0)$.   Condition (1)

Let $\mathbf{v}_1 = (x_1, 3x_1)$ and $\mathbf{v}_2 = (x_2, 3x_2)$ belong to S. Then   Condition (2)

$$\begin{aligned} \mathbf{v}_1 + \mathbf{v}_2 &= (x_1, 3x_1) + (x_2, 3x_2) \\ &= (x_1 + x_2, 3x_1 + 3x_2) \\ &= (x_1 + x_2, 3(x_1 + x_2)). \end{aligned}$$

This vector has the correct form for a vector in S, since $x_1 + x_2 \in \mathbb{R}$, so S is closed under vector addition.

Let $\mathbf{v} = (x, 3x) \in S$ and $\alpha \in \mathbb{R}$. Then   Condition (3)

$$\alpha\mathbf{v} = \alpha(x, 3x) = (\alpha x, \alpha 3x) = (\alpha x, 3(\alpha x)).$$

This vector has the correct form for a vector in S, since $\alpha x \in \mathbb{R}$, so S is closed under scalar multiplication.

Since conditions (1), (2) and (3) are satisfied, S is a subspace of $\mathbb{R}^2$. This subspace is the line through the origin with equation $y = 3x$.   ∎

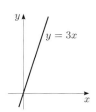

41

Exercise 4.1 Show that the set of vectors $S = \{(x, -2x) : x \in \mathbb{R}\}$ is a subspace of $\mathbb{R}^2$.

Example 4.2   Show that the set of vectors $S = \{(x, y, 2x - 3y) : x, y \in \mathbb{R}\}$ is a subspace of $\mathbb{R}^3$.

Solution   We use Strategy 4.1.

S contains the zero vector of $\mathbb{R}^3$: choosing $x = y = 0$ gives $(0, 0, 0)$.   Condition (1)

Let $\mathbf{v}_1 = (x_1, y_1, 2x_1 - 3y_1)$ and $\mathbf{v}_2 = (x_2, y_2, 2x_2 - 3y_2)$ belong to S. Then   Condition (2)

$$\begin{aligned}
\mathbf{v}_1 + \mathbf{v}_2 &= (x_1, y_1, 2x_1 - 3y_1) + (x_2, y_2, 2x_2 - 3y_2) \\
&= (x_1 + x_2, y_1 + y_2, 2x_1 - 3y_1 + 2x_2 - 3y_2) \\
&= (x_1 + x_2, y_1 + y_2, 2(x_1 + x_2) - 3(y_1 + y_2)).
\end{aligned}$$

This vector has the correct form for a vector in S, since $x_1 + x_2 \in \mathbb{R}$ and $y_1 + y_2 \in \mathbb{R}$, so S is closed under vector addition.

Let $\mathbf{v} = (x, y, 2x - 3y) \in S$ and $\alpha \in \mathbb{R}$. Then   Condition (3)

$$\begin{aligned}
\alpha \mathbf{v} &= \alpha(x, y, 2x - 3y) \\
&= (\alpha x, \alpha y, \alpha(2x - 3y)) \\
&= (\alpha x, \alpha y, 2(\alpha x) - 3(\alpha y)).
\end{aligned}$$

This vector has the correct form for a vector in S, since $\alpha x \in \mathbb{R}$ and $\alpha y \in \mathbb{R}$, so S is closed under scalar multiplication.

Since conditions (1), (2) and (3) are satisfied, S is a subspace of $\mathbb{R}^3$. It is the plane through the origin with equation $2x - 3y - z = 0$. ∎

$2x - 3y - z = 0$

Example 4.3

Show that the set of vectors $S = \{(x, y, x - y + 2) : x, y \in \mathbb{R}\}$ is not a subspace of $\mathbb{R}^3$.

Solution   As before, we use Strategy 4.1.

If $\mathbf{0} \in S$, then $(x, y, x - y + 2) = (0, 0, 0)$ for some numbers x and y; that is,

$$\begin{cases} x & = 0, \\ y & = 0, \\ x - y + 2 & = 0. \end{cases}$$

There are no values of x and y that simultaneously satisfy these three equations, so $\mathbf{0}$ does not belong to S. So condition (1) is not satisfied, and hence S is not a subspace of $\mathbb{R}^3$. ∎

Since condition (1) is not satisfied, we do not need to check conditions (2) and (3).

Exercise 4.2 For each of the following, determine whether the set S is a subspace of the vector space V.

(a) $V = \mathbb{R}^2$, $S = \{(x, x + 2) : x \in \mathbb{R}\}$.

(b) $V = \mathbb{R}^3$, $S = \{(z - y, y, z) : y, z \in \mathbb{R}\}$.

(c) $V = \mathbb{R}^4$, $S = \{(x, y, z, x + 2y - z) : x, y, z \in \mathbb{R}\}$.

Example 4.4   Show that the set $S = \{a \cos x : a \in \mathbb{R}\}$ is a subspace of the vector space $V = \{a \cos x + b \sin x : a, b \in \mathbb{R}\}$.

We showed that V is a vector space in Example 1.3.

Solution   We use Strategy 4.1.

S contains the zero vector, as choosing $a = 0$ gives $a \cos x = 0 \cos x = 0$.   Condition(1)

Let $f_1(x) = a_1 \cos x$ and $f_2(x) = a_2 \cos x$. Then   Condition(2)

$$f_1(x) + f_2(x) = a_1 \cos x + a_2 \cos x = (a_1 + a_2) \cos x.$$

The function $f_1(x) + f_2(x)$ has the correct form for a vector in S, so S is closed under vector addition.

Let $f(x) = a \cos x$ and $\alpha \in \mathbb{R}$. Then   Condition(3)

$$\alpha f(x) = \alpha a \cos x = (\alpha a) \cos x.$$

This function has the correct form for a vector in S, so S is closed under scalar multiplication.

Thus S is a subspace of V.   ■

Exercise 4.3   For each of the following, determine whether the set S is a subspace of the vector space V.

(a) $V = P_3, \quad S = \{a + bx : a, b \in \mathbb{R}\}$.

(b) $V = P_3, \quad S = \{x + ax^2 : a \in \mathbb{R}\}$.

(c) $V = M_{2,2}, \quad S = \left\{ \begin{pmatrix} a & 1 \\ 0 & d \end{pmatrix} : a, d \in \mathbb{R} \right\}$.

The following theorem shows that the span of a subset of a vector space is always a subspace.

Theorem 4.2   Let S be a non-empty finite subset of a vector space V. Then $\langle S \rangle$ is a subspace of V.

Proof   We use Strategy 4.1.

Let $S = \{\mathbf{u}_1, \mathbf{u}_2, \dots, \mathbf{u}_n\}$ be a non-empty finite subset of a vector space V.

$\langle S \rangle$ contains the zero vector, since $0\mathbf{u}_1 + 0\mathbf{u}_2 + \cdots + 0\mathbf{u}_n = \mathbf{0}$ belongs to $\langle S \rangle$.

Let $\mathbf{v}_1 = \alpha_1 \mathbf{u}_1 + \alpha_2 \mathbf{u}_2 + \cdots + \alpha_n \mathbf{u}_n$ and $\mathbf{v}_2 = \beta_1 \mathbf{u}_1 + \beta_2 \mathbf{u}_2 + \cdots + \beta_n \mathbf{u}_n$ be any two vectors in $\langle S \rangle$. Then

$$\mathbf{v}_1 + \mathbf{v}_2 = (\alpha_1 \mathbf{u}_1 + \alpha_2 \mathbf{u}_2 + \cdots + \alpha_n \mathbf{u}_n) + (\beta_1 \mathbf{u}_1 + \beta_2 \mathbf{u}_2 + \cdots + \beta_n \mathbf{u}_n)$$
$$= (\alpha_1 + \beta_1)\mathbf{u}_1 + (\alpha_2 + \beta_2)\mathbf{u}_2 + \cdots + (\alpha_n + \beta_n)\mathbf{u}_n.$$

This is a member of $\langle S \rangle$, since it is a linear combination of $\mathbf{u}_1, \mathbf{u}_2, \dots, \mathbf{u}_n$. Hence $\langle S \rangle$ is closed under vector addition.

Let $\mathbf{v} = \alpha_1 \mathbf{u}_1 + \alpha_2 \mathbf{u}_2 + \cdots + \alpha_n \mathbf{u}_n$ and $\alpha \in \mathbb{R}$. Then

$$\alpha \mathbf{v} = \alpha(\alpha_1 \mathbf{u}_1 + \alpha_2 \mathbf{u}_2 + \cdots + \alpha_n \mathbf{u}_n)$$
$$= (\alpha \alpha_1)\mathbf{u}_1 + (\alpha \alpha_2)\mathbf{u}_2 + \cdots + (\alpha \alpha_n)\mathbf{u}_n.$$

This is a member of $\langle S \rangle$, since it is a linear combination of $\mathbf{u}_1, \mathbf{u}_2, \dots, \mathbf{u}_n$. Hence $\langle S \rangle$ is closed under scalar multiplication.

Thus $\langle S \rangle$ is a subspace of V.   ■

4.2 Bases and dimension

In the previous subsection you saw several subspaces of finite-dimensional vector spaces. Since these subspaces are all vector spaces in their own right, they have bases and dimensions, and we look at these in this subsection.

Let us return to two of our earlier examples from Section 2, Examples 2.8(a) and (b).

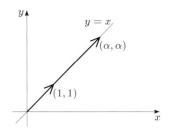

In Example 2.8(a), by Theorem 4.2, the set of vectors in $\mathbb{R}^2$ spanned by the set $S = \{(1,1)\}$ is a subspace of $\mathbb{R}^2$. We saw that any vector in the subspace $\langle S \rangle$ can be written in the form (α, α) for some $\alpha \in \mathbb{R}$, so $\{(1,1)\}$ is a basis for this subspace. Thus the dimension of the subspace is 1. This agrees with our geometric idea of dimension, as we saw that these vectors form a line through the origin—the line $y = x$, which is one-dimensional.

In Examples 2.8(b), the set of vectors in $\mathbb{R}^3$ spanned by the set $S = \{(1,0,1),(2,0,3)\}$ is a subspace of $\mathbb{R}^3$. The subspace $\langle S \rangle$ consists of those points of $\mathbb{R}^3$ of the form $(x, 0, z)$. Since the set $\{(1,0,1),(2,0,3)\}$ spans the subspace and is linearly independent (the vectors are not multiples of each other), it is a basis for the subspace. Since there are two vectors in the basis, the dimension of the subspace is 2. Linking the idea of dimension in linear algebra and our geometric idea of dimension, we see that the subspace spanned by these two vectors is a plane through the origin—namely, the plane $y = 0$—which is two-dimensional. Since any vector in the subspace can be written in the form $(x, 0, z)$, we can find another basis for this subspace by writing

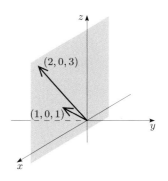

$$(x, 0, z) = x(1,0,0) + z(0,0,1).$$

This means that the set $\{(1,0,0),(0,0,1)\}$ is a spanning set for the subspace and, as it is also linearly independent, it is a basis for the subspace. This basis has the additional advantage that it is *orthogonal*, which means that the basis vectors are at right angles to each other.

Orthogonal bases will be discussed in Section 5.

Example 4.5   Find the equation of the subspace of $\mathbb{R}^3$ spanned by the set $\{(1,0,2),(2,3,4)\}$.

Solution   Since $\{(1,0,2),(2,3,4)\}$ is a linearly independent set, the subspace it spans is a two-dimensional subspace of $\mathbb{R}^3$, and is therefore a plane through the origin with equation

$$ax + by + cz = 0,$$

where a, b, c are not all zero.

Since the vectors in the spanning set lie in the plane, the values of a, b and c must satisfy the simultaneous equations

$$\begin{cases} a \quad\ \ + 2c = 0, \\ 2a + 3b + 4c = 0. \end{cases}$$

The first of these equations gives $a = -2c$, and substituting this into the second equation gives $b = 0$, so the subspace is the plane with equation $-2cx + cz = 0$, or, equivalently,

$$2x - z = 0. \quad \blacksquare$$

Exercise 4.4   Find the equation of the subspace of $\mathbb{R}^3$ spanned by the set $\{(1, -2, 0),(0, 3, 3)\}$.

Example 4.6   Find a basis for the subspace $S = \{(z - y, y, z) : y, z \in \mathbb{R}\}$ of $\mathbb{R}^3$, and hence write down the dimension of S.

You showed that S is a subspace of $\mathbb{R}^3$ in Exercise 4.2(b).

Solution   We use the form of the vectors in S to help us find a possible basis. Since

$$(z - y, y, z) = z(1, 0, 1) + y(-1, 1, 0),$$

any vector in S can be written as a linear combination of the vectors in the set $\{(1, 0, 1), (-1, 1, 0)\}$, so this set spans S. The vectors in the set are also linearly independent, as they are not multiples of each other, so $\{(1, 0, 1), (-1, 1, 0)\}$ is a basis for S. Therefore S has dimension 2.   ∎

Exercise 4.5   Find a basis for the subspace

$$S = \{(x, y, z, x + 2y - z) : x, y, z \in \mathbb{R}\}$$

of $\mathbb{R}^4$, and hence write down the dimension of S.

You showed that S is a subspace of $\mathbb{R}^4$ in Exercise 4.2(c).

Example 4.7   Find a basis for the plane $x - 3y + 2z = 0$ (a subspace of $\mathbb{R}^3$).

Solution   Since the subspace is a plane, it has dimension 2, and so has two basis vectors. We need to find two vectors that lie in the plane and form a linearly independent set. There are many choices, but $(0, 2, 3)$ and $(3, 1, 0)$ both lie in the plane, and are clearly linearly independent, as one is not a multiple of the other, so $\{(0, 2, 3), (3, 1, 0)\}$ is a basis for the subspace $x - 3y + 2z = 0$.   ∎

You will see more examples like this in Section 5.

The following result, which will be used in Unit LA4, has been illustrated by examples and exercises in this section. For example, in Example 4.6 $\dim V = 3$ and $\dim S = 2$.

Unit LA4, Section 4.

> **Theorem 4.3**   The dimension of a subspace of a vector space V is less than or equal to the dimension of V.

Proof   Let V be a vector space of dimension n, and let S be a subspace of V. Suppose that the dimension of S is m, and let $\{\mathbf{e}_1, \ldots, \mathbf{e}_m\}$ be a basis for S. Then $\{\mathbf{e}_1, \ldots, \mathbf{e}_m\}$ is a linearly independent set of vectors in V. Thus $m \leq n$ by the corollary to Theorem 3.3.   ∎

Further exercises

Exercise 4.6   Prove Theorem 4.1 by considering each of the axioms in the definition of a vector space and showing that they are true for a subset of a vector space if the conditions of Theorem 4.1 are satisfied.

The theorem is stated on page 41.

Exercise 4.7 Determine whether each of the following subsets S is a subspace of the given vector space V.

(a) $V = \mathbb{R}^3$, $S = \{(x, y, 2x + y) : x, y \in \mathbb{R}\}$.

(b) $V = \mathbb{R}^2$, $S = \{(x, x - 3) : x \in \mathbb{R}\}$.

(c) $V = \mathbb{R}^4$, $S = \{(x, y, x - 3y, 2x + y) : x, y \in \mathbb{R}\}$.

(d) $V = P_3$, $S = \{ax^2 : a \in \mathbb{R}\}$.

(e) $V = M_{3,1}$, $S = \left\langle \left\{ \begin{pmatrix} 1 \\ 0 \\ 3 \end{pmatrix}, \begin{pmatrix} -1 \\ 2 \\ 0 \end{pmatrix} \right\} \right\rangle$.

(f) $V = \mathbb{R}^2$, $S = \{(x, y) : x \geq 0, \ y \geq 0, \ x, y \in \mathbb{R}\}$.

Exercise 4.8 Find a basis, and hence the dimension, for each of the subspaces in Exercise 4.7.

5   Orthogonal bases

After working through this section, you should be able to:

(a) check whether the vectors in a given set are *orthogonal*;

(b) express a given vector in terms of an *orthogonal basis*;

(c) find orthogonal bases for $\mathbb{R}^n$, and for subspaces of $\mathbb{R}^n$ satisfying specified conditions.

5.1 Orthogonal bases in $\mathbb{R}^2$, $\mathbb{R}^3$ and $\mathbb{R}^4$

Suppose that we wish to express the vector $(10, 0, 4)$ in $\mathbb{R}^3$ in terms of the basis

$$\{(2, 1, 1), (1, -4, 2), (-2, 1, 3)\}.$$

Using the method given in Section 2, we first write

$$(10, 0, 4) = \alpha_1(2, 1, 1) + \alpha_2(1, -4, 2) + \alpha_3(-2, 1, 3).$$

Equating corresponding coordinates, we obtain the simultaneous equations

$$\begin{cases} 2\alpha_1 + \ \alpha_2 - 2\alpha_3 = 10, \\ \ \alpha_1 - 4\alpha_2 + \ \alpha_3 = \ \ 0, \\ \ \alpha_1 + 2\alpha_2 + 3\alpha_3 = \ \ 4. \end{cases}$$

Using the methods of Unit LA2, we can solve these equations and, after much algebra, we obtain the solution

$$\alpha_1 = 4, \quad \alpha_2 = \tfrac{6}{7}, \quad \alpha_3 = -\tfrac{4}{7}.$$

Thus

$$(10, 0, 4) = 4(2, 1, 1) + \tfrac{6}{7}(1, -4, 2) - \tfrac{4}{7}(-2, 1, 3).$$

The above method involves finding the solution of a system of linear equations. In this section we show that there is a simpler method which can be used when, as here, the given basis is an *orthogonal* basis.

We start by reminding you of the definitions of the dot product and orthogonality in $\mathbb{R}^2$.

Unit LA1, Section 3.

> **Definitions**   Let $\mathbf{v}_1 = (x_1, y_1)$ and $\mathbf{v}_2 = (x_2, y_2)$ be vectors in $\mathbb{R}^2$.
>
> The **dot product** of $\mathbf{v}_1$ and $\mathbf{v}_2$ is the real number
>
> $\quad \mathbf{v}_1 \cdot \mathbf{v}_2 = x_1 x_2 + y_1 y_2.$
>
> The vectors $\mathbf{v}_1$ and $\mathbf{v}_2$ are **orthogonal** if $\mathbf{v}_1 \cdot \mathbf{v}_2 = 0$.

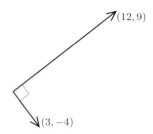

For example, the vectors $\mathbf{v}_1 = (3, -4)$ and $\mathbf{v}_2 = (12, 9)$ are orthogonal, since

$\quad \mathbf{v}_1 \cdot \mathbf{v}_2 = (3 \times 12) + ((-4) \times 9) = 36 - 36 = 0.$

Geometrically, this means that the vectors $\mathbf{v}_1$ and $\mathbf{v}_2$ are at right angles.

> **Exercise 5.1**   Determine which pairs of the following vectors are orthogonal:
>
> $\quad \mathbf{v}_1 = (-2, 6), \quad \mathbf{v}_2 = (9, 3), \quad \mathbf{v}_3 = (5, -15).$

In the audio section we extend these ideas to $\mathbb{R}^3$ and $\mathbb{R}^4$. We first define an orthogonal set in $\mathbb{R}^3$, and show that such a set must be linearly independent; this leads to the idea of an orthogonal basis for $\mathbb{R}^3$. We then show that we can use dot products to express any given vector in terms of such a basis without having to solve a system of simultaneous equations. We also show how an orthogonal basis can be constructed for any subspace of $\mathbb{R}^3$ and then extended to a basis for $\mathbb{R}^3$. Finally, we demonstrate how these ideas can be extended to $\mathbb{R}^4$.

Listen to the audio as you work through the frames.

Audio

47

1. Orthogonal vectors in $\mathbb{R}^3$

Definition   The vectors $\underline{v}_1 = (x_1, y_1, z_1)$ and $\underline{v}_2 = (x_2, y_2, z_2)$ in $\mathbb{R}^3$ are **orthogonal** if

$$\underline{v}_1 \cdot \underline{v}_2 = x_1 x_2 + y_1 y_2 + z_1 z_2 = 0.$$

For example,

(2, 1, 1) and (1, −4, 2) are orthogonal,

since

$$(2 \times 1) + (1 \times (-4)) + (1 \times 2) = 2 - 4 + 2 = 0.$$

defined in terms of dot product

2. Orthogonal sets in $\mathbb{R}^3$

Definition   A set of vectors in $\mathbb{R}^3$ is an **orthogonal set** if any two distinct vectors in the set are orthogonal.

For example,

$\{\underline{v}_1, \underline{v}_2\}$ is an orthogonal set if $\underline{v}_1 \cdot \underline{v}_2 = 0$,

so $\{(2, 1, 1), (1, -4, 2)\}$ is an orthogonal set.

Similarly,

$\{\underline{v}_1, \underline{v}_2, \underline{v}_3\}$ is an orthogonal set if $\underline{v}_1 \cdot \underline{v}_2 = \underline{v}_1 \cdot \underline{v}_3 = \underline{v}_2 \cdot \underline{v}_3 = 0$,

so $\{(2, 1, 1), (1, -4, 2), (-2, 1, 3)\}$ is an orthogonal set

since

$(2, 1, 1) \cdot (1, -4, 2) = 0$,

$(2, 1, 1) \cdot (-2, 1, 3) = -4 + 1 + 3 = 0$,

$(1, -4, 2) \cdot (-2, 1, 3) = -2 - 4 + 6 = 0.$

3. Linear independence of orthogonal sets in $\mathbb{R}^3$

Theorem

Let $\{\underline{v}_1, \underline{v}_2, \underline{v}_3\}$ be an orthogonal set of non-zero vectors in $\mathbb{R}^3$. Then $\underline{v}_1$, $\underline{v}_2$ and $\underline{v}_3$ are linearly independent.

want to show $\alpha_1 = \alpha_2 = \alpha_3 = 0$

Proof

Suppose that

$$\alpha_1 \underline{v}_1 + \alpha_2 \underline{v}_2 + \alpha_3 \underline{v}_3 = \underline{0}.$$

We know that

$$\underline{v}_1 \cdot \underline{v}_1 \neq 0, \quad \underline{v}_1 \cdot \underline{v}_2 = 0, \quad \underline{v}_1 \cdot \underline{v}_3 = 0,$$

so we form the dot product of both sides of the equation with $\underline{v}_1$:

$$\underline{v}_1 \cdot (\alpha_1 \underline{v}_1 + \alpha_2 \underline{v}_2 + \alpha_3 \underline{v}_3) = \underline{v}_1 \cdot \underline{0} = 0.$$

We obtain

$$\alpha_1 (\underline{v}_1 \cdot \underline{v}_1) + \alpha_2 (\underline{v}_1 \cdot \underline{v}_2) + \alpha_3 (\underline{v}_1 \cdot \underline{v}_3) = 0,$$

≠ 0   *= 0*   *= 0*

hence $\alpha_1 = 0$.

Similarly, we form the dot product with $\underline{v}_2$ and with $\underline{v}_3$:

$\underline{v}_2 \cdot (\alpha_1 \underline{v}_1 + \alpha_2 \underline{v}_2 + \alpha_3 \underline{v}_3) = 0$, giving $\alpha_2 = 0$;

$\underline{v}_3 \cdot (\alpha_1 \underline{v}_1 + \alpha_2 \underline{v}_2 + \alpha_3 \underline{v}_3) = 0$, giving $\alpha_3 = 0$.

So if $\alpha_1 \underline{v}_1 + \alpha_2 \underline{v}_2 + \alpha_3 \underline{v}_3 = 0$, then $\alpha_1 = \alpha_2 = \alpha_3 = 0$.

Thus

$\{\underline{v}_1, \underline{v}_2, \underline{v}_3\}$ is a linearly independent set.

4. Orthogonal bases

Theorem

Any orthogonal set of three non-zero vectors in $\mathbb{R}^3$ is an orthogonal basis for $\mathbb{R}^3$.

For example,

$\{(1,0,0), (0,1,0), (0,0,1)\}$,

$\{(2,1,1), (1,-4,2), (-2,1,3)\}$

are orthogonal bases for $\mathbb{R}^3$.

> A linearly independent set of three vectors in $\mathbb{R}^3$ is a basis for $\mathbb{R}^3$

Frame 3

Frame 2

5. Using orthogonal bases: a specific case

Express $(10,0,4)$ in terms of the orthogonal basis $\{(2,1,1), (1,-4,2), (-2,1,3)\}$.

Let $(10,0,4) = \alpha_1(2,1,1) + \alpha_2(1,-4,2) + \alpha_3(-2,1,3)$.

We take the dot product with each basis vector in turn.

$(2,1,1)\cdot(10,0,4) = \alpha_1(2,1,1)\cdot(2,1,1) + 0 + 0$,

thus $24 = 6\alpha_1$, so $\boxed{\alpha_1 = 4}$.

$(1,-4,2)\cdot(10,0,4) = \alpha_2(1,-4,2)\cdot(1,-4,2)$,

thus $18 = 21\alpha_2$, so $\boxed{\alpha_2 = \frac{6}{7}}$.

$(-2,1,3)\cdot(10,0,4) = \alpha_3(-2,1,3)\cdot(-2,1,3)$,

thus $-8 = 14\alpha_3$, so $\boxed{\alpha_3 = -\frac{4}{7}}$.

Thus $(10,0,4) = 4(2,1,1) + \frac{6}{7}(1,-4,2) - \frac{4}{7}(-2,1,3)$.

6. Using orthogonal bases: general case

Strategy (generalised in Strategy 5.3)

To express $\underline{u} \in \mathbb{R}^3$ in terms of the orthogonal basis $\{\underline{v}_1, \underline{v}_2, \underline{v}_3\}$.

Let

$$\underline{u} = \alpha_1\underline{v}_1 + \alpha_2\underline{v}_2 + \alpha_3\underline{v}_3.$$

Then

$$\underline{v}_1\cdot\underline{u} = \alpha_1\,(\underline{v}_1\cdot\underline{v}_1) + \alpha_2\,(\underline{v}_1\cdot\underline{v}_2) + \alpha_3\,(\underline{v}_1\cdot\underline{v}_3).$$

($\neq 0$, $=0$, $=0$)

Thus

$$\underline{v}_1\cdot\underline{u} = \alpha_1\,(\underline{v}_1\cdot\underline{v}_1), \qquad \text{so} \qquad \boxed{\alpha_1 = \frac{\underline{v}_1\cdot\underline{u}}{\underline{v}_1\cdot\underline{v}_1}}.$$

Similarly,

$$\underline{v}_2\cdot\underline{u} = \alpha_2\,(\underline{v}_2\cdot\underline{v}_2), \qquad \text{so} \qquad \boxed{\alpha_2 = \frac{\underline{v}_2\cdot\underline{u}}{\underline{v}_2\cdot\underline{v}_2}};$$

$$\underline{v}_3\cdot\underline{u} = \alpha_3\,(\underline{v}_3\cdot\underline{v}_3), \qquad \text{so} \qquad \boxed{\alpha_3 = \frac{\underline{v}_3\cdot\underline{u}}{\underline{v}_3\cdot\underline{v}_3}}.$$

Thus

$$\underline{u} = \left(\frac{\underline{v}_1\cdot\underline{u}}{\underline{v}_1\cdot\underline{v}_1}\right)\underline{v}_1 + \left(\frac{\underline{v}_2\cdot\underline{u}}{\underline{v}_2\cdot\underline{v}_2}\right)\underline{v}_2 + \left(\frac{\underline{v}_3\cdot\underline{u}}{\underline{v}_3\cdot\underline{v}_3}\right)\underline{v}_3.$$

7. Exercise 5.2

(a) Verify that $\{(3,4,0), (8,-6,0), (0,0,5)\}$ is an orthogonal basis for $\mathbb{R}^3$.

(b) Express the vector $(10,0,4)$ in terms of this basis.

8. Extending an orthogonal set in $\mathbb{R}^3$

Solution in Frame 11

Find an orthogonal basis for $\mathbb{R}^3$ containing $(2, 1, 1)$.

Strategy 5.1

To find an orthogonal basis for $\mathbb{R}^3$ containing a given vector.

Find a plane which is orthogonal to the given vector, and then find an orthogonal basis for the plane.

$(2, 1, 1) \cdot (x, y, z) = 0$

We choose the plane $2x + y + z = 0$.

9. Finding orthogonal basis for subspace of $\mathbb{R}^3$:

Method 1

Frame 8

Find an orthogonal basis $\{\underline{v}_1, \underline{v}_2\}$ for the plane

$2x + y + z = 0$.

METHOD 1

First basis vector: Take any non-zero vector in the plane.

For example, take $\underline{v}_1 = (1, -2, 0)$.

Second basis vector: Let $\underline{v}_2 = (x, y, z)$.

Now we want $\underline{v}_1$ and $\underline{v}_2$ to be orthogonal, so $x - 2y \quad = 0$,   (1)

and $\underline{v}_2$ lies in the plane, so $2x + y + z = 0$.   (2)

From (1), $x = 2y$.

From (2), $4y + y + z = 0$, so $z = -5y$.

Thus any non-zero vector $(2y, y, -5y)$ will do for $\underline{v}_2$.

For example, take $\underline{v}_2 = (2, 1, -5)$.

So an orthogonal basis for this plane is $\{(1, -2, 0), (2, 1, -5)\}$.

10. Finding orthogonal basis for subspace of $\mathbb{R}^3$:

Method 2

Frame 8

Find an orthogonal basis $\{\underline{v}_1, \underline{v}_2\}$ for the plane

$2x + y + z = 0$.

METHOD 2   First choose any basis for the given plane.

For example, $\{(1, -2, 0), (1, 0, -2)\}$.

First basis vector: Take $\underline{v}_1 = (1, -2, 0)$.

Second basis vector: Take $\underline{v}_2 = (1, 0, -2) - \alpha \underline{v}_1$.

Now we want $\underline{v}_1$ and $\underline{v}_2$ to be orthogonal, so

$\underline{v}_1 \cdot \underline{v}_2 = (1, -2, 0) \cdot (1, 0, -2) - \alpha \, (1, -2, 0) \cdot (1, -2, 0) = 0.$

Thus $1 - 5\alpha = 0,$

so $\alpha = \frac{1}{5}$ and $\underline{v}_2 = (1, 0, -2) - \frac{1}{5} (1, -2, 0),$

that is, $\underline{v}_2 = \left(\frac{4}{5}, \frac{2}{5}, -2 \right).$

So an orthogonal basis for this plane is $\left\{ (1, -2, 0), \left(\frac{4}{5}, \frac{2}{5}, -2 \right) \right\}.$

11. Solution to problem posed in Frame 8

Frame 9
Frame 10

We have found an orthogonal basis for $\mathbb{R}^3$ containing $(2, 1, 1)$ by two methods.

Method 1 gives the orthogonal basis

$\{(2, 1, 1), (1, -2, 0), (2, 1, -5)\}.$

Method 2 gives the orthogonal basis

$\left\{ (2, 1, 1), (1, -2, 0), \left(\frac{4}{5}, \frac{2}{5}, -2 \right) \right\}.$

12. Exercise 5.3

Find an orthogonal basis for $\mathbb{R}^3$ containing $(3, -4, 5)$.

13. Orthogonality in $\mathbb{R}^4$

Definition   The vectors $\underline{v}_1 = (x_1, y_1, z_1, w_1)$ and $\underline{v}_2 = (x_2, y_2, z_2, w_2)$ in $\mathbb{R}^4$ are **orthogonal** if
$$\underline{v}_1 \cdot \underline{v}_2 = x_1 x_2 + y_1 y_2 + z_1 z_2 + w_1 w_2 = 0.$$

(defined in terms of dot product)

Definition   A set of vectors in $\mathbb{R}^4$ is an **orthogonal set** if any two distinct vectors in the set are orthogonal.

So
$$\{\underline{v}_1, \underline{v}_2, \underline{v}_3, \underline{v}_4\} \text{ is an orthogonal set}$$

if
$$\underline{v}_1 \cdot \underline{v}_2 = \underline{v}_1 \cdot \underline{v}_3 = \underline{v}_1 \cdot \underline{v}_4 = \underline{v}_2 \cdot \underline{v}_3 = \underline{v}_2 \cdot \underline{v}_4 = \underline{v}_3 \cdot \underline{v}_4 = 0.$$

Theorem

Any orthogonal set of four non-zero vectors in $\mathbb{R}^4$ is an orthogonal basis for $\mathbb{R}^4$.

(Proof as in Frames 3 and 4)

14. Extending an orthogonal set in $\mathbb{R}^4$

Find an orthogonal basis for $\mathbb{R}^4$ containing $(1, 2, -5, -1)$.

Strategy 5.2

To find an orthogonal basis for $\mathbb{R}^4$ containing a given vector.

Find a hyperplane which is orthogonal to the given vector, and then find an orthogonal basis for the hyperplane.

(a hyperplane is a three-dimensional subspace of $\mathbb{R}^4$)

We choose the hyperplane
$$x + 2y - 5z - w = 0.$$

($(x, y, z, w) \cdot (1, 2, -5, -1) = 0$)

15. Finding orthogonal basis for subspace of $\mathbb{R}^4$

Find an orthogonal basis $\{\underline{v}_1, \underline{v}_2, \underline{v}_3\}$ for the hyperplane $x + 2y - 5z - w = 0$.

(Method 2 is better for dimensions higher than 2)

First choose any basis for the given hyperplane. For example,
$$\{(2, -1, 0, 0), (5, 0, 1, 0), (1, 0, 0, 1)\}.$$

First basis vector: Take $\underline{v}_1 = \boxed{(2, -1, 0, 0)}$.

Second basis vector: Take $\underline{v}_2 = (5, 0, 1, 0) - \alpha \underline{v}_1$.

Now we want $\underline{v}_1$ and $\underline{v}_2$ to be orthogonal, so
$$\underline{v}_1 \cdot \underline{v}_2 = (2, -1, 0, 0) \cdot (5, 0, 1, 0) - \alpha (2, -1, 0, 0) \cdot (2, -1, 0, 0) = 0.$$

Thus $\quad 10 - 5\alpha = 0,$

so $\quad \alpha = 2$ and $\underline{v}_2 = (5, 0, 1, 0) - 2(2, -1, 0, 0),$

that is, $\qquad \underline{v}_2 = \boxed{(1, 2, 1, 0)}$.

Third basis vector: Take $\underline{v}_3 = (1, 0, 0, 1) - \beta_1 \underline{v}_1 - \beta_2 \underline{v}_2$.

Now we want $\underline{v}_1$ and $\underline{v}_2$ to be orthogonal to $\underline{v}_3$, so
$$\underline{v}_1 \cdot \underline{v}_3 = (2, -1, 0, 0) \cdot (1, 0, 0, 1) - \beta_1 (2, -1, 0, 0) \cdot (2, -1, 0, 0) = 0,$$

giving $2 - 5\beta_1 = 0,$ so $\beta_1 = \dfrac{2}{5},$

and
$$\underline{v}_2 \cdot \underline{v}_3 = (1, 2, 1, 0) \cdot (1, 0, 0, 1) - \beta_2 (1, 2, 1, 0) \cdot (1, 2, 1, 0) = 0,$$

giving $1 - 6\beta_2 = 0,$ so $\beta_2 = \dfrac{1}{6}.$

Therefore $\underline{v}_3 = (1, 0, 0, 1) - \dfrac{2}{5} (2, -1, 0, 0) - \dfrac{1}{6} (1, 2, 1, 0),$

that is, $\qquad \underline{v}_3 = \boxed{\left(\dfrac{1}{30}, \dfrac{1}{15}, -\dfrac{1}{6}, 1\right)}.$

Thus an orthogonal basis for the hyperplane is $\{\underline{v}_1, \underline{v}_2, \underline{v}_3\}$, and an orthogonal basis for $\mathbb{R}^4$ is
$$\left\{(1, 2, -5, -1), (2, -1, 0, 0), (1, 2, 1, 0), \left(\dfrac{1}{30}, \dfrac{1}{15}, -\dfrac{1}{6}, 1\right)\right\}.$$

5.2 Orthogonal bases in $\mathbb{R}^n$

In this subsection we show how the definitions and results of Subsection 5.1 can be generalised to $\mathbb{R}^n$, for any positive integer n. We start with the definition of the dot product of vectors.

Definition   Let $\mathbf{v} = (v_1, v_2, \ldots, v_n)$ and $\mathbf{w} = (w_1, w_2, \ldots, w_n)$ be vectors in $\mathbb{R}^n$. The **dot product** of $\mathbf{v}$ and $\mathbf{w}$ is the real number

$$\mathbf{v} \cdot \mathbf{w} = v_1 w_1 + v_2 w_2 + \cdots + v_n w_n.$$

For example, in $\mathbb{R}^5$ the dot product of the vectors $\mathbf{v} = (1, 2, 3, 4, 5)$ and $\mathbf{w} = (3, -4, 0, 3, -2)$ is

$$\mathbf{v} \cdot \mathbf{w} = (1 \times 3) + (2 \times (-4)) + (3 \times 0) + (4 \times 3) + (5 \times (-2))$$
$$= 3 - 8 + 0 + 12 - 10 = -3.$$

Exercise 5.4   Calculate the following dot products.

(a) $(1, 2, -1, 0) \cdot (0, -5, 6, -3)$ in $\mathbb{R}^4$.

(b) $(1, 2, 3, 4, 5, 6) \cdot (3, 2, 1, 0, -1, -2)$ in $\mathbb{R}^6$.

We next extend the ideas of an orthogonal set and an orthogonal basis to $\mathbb{R}^n$.

Definitions   The vectors $\mathbf{v}$ and $\mathbf{w}$ in $\mathbb{R}^n$ are **orthogonal** if $\mathbf{v} \cdot \mathbf{w} = 0$.

A set of vectors in $\mathbb{R}^n$ is an **orthogonal set** if any two distinct vectors in the set are orthogonal.

An **orthogonal basis** for $\mathbb{R}^n$ is an orthogonal set which is a basis for $\mathbb{R}^n$.

For example, in $\mathbb{R}^6$ the set

$$\{(1, 1, 1, 1, 1, 1), (2, -2, 2, -2, 2, -2), (5, 5, 0, 0, -5, -5)\}$$

is an orthogonal set, since

$$(1, 1, 1, 1, 1, 1) \cdot (2, -2, 2, -2, 2, -2) = 2 - 2 + 2 - 2 + 2 - 2 = 0,$$
$$(1, 1, 1, 1, 1, 1) \cdot (5, 5, 0, 0, -5, -5) = 5 + 5 + 0 + 0 - 5 - 5 = 0$$

and

$$(2, -2, 2, -2, 2, -2) \cdot (5, 5, 0, 0, -5, -5)$$
$$= 10 - 10 + 0 + 0 - 10 + 10 = 0.$$

Note that the standard basis

$$\{(1, 0, 0, \ldots, 0), (0, 1, 0, \ldots, 0), (0, 0, 1, \ldots, 0), \ldots, (0, 0, 0, \ldots, 1)\}$$

is an orthogonal basis for $\mathbb{R}^n$.

In the audio section you saw that any orthogonal set of three non-zero vectors in $\mathbb{R}^3$ is linearly independent and therefore forms an orthogonal basis for $\mathbb{R}^3$. By using the same ideas, we can prove the following more general result.

Theorem 5.1   Let $S = \{\mathbf{v}_1, \mathbf{v}_2, \ldots, \mathbf{v}_k\}$ be an orthogonal set of non-zero vectors in $\mathbb{R}^n$. Then S is a linearly independent set.

Proof   Let $S = \{\mathbf{v}_1, \mathbf{v}_2, \ldots, \mathbf{v}_k\}$ be an orthogonal set of non-zero vectors in $\mathbb{R}^n$. In order to prove that S is a linearly independent set, we need to show that the only solution of the equation

$$\alpha_1 \mathbf{v}_1 + \alpha_2 \mathbf{v}_2 + \cdots + \alpha_k \mathbf{v}_k = \mathbf{0}$$

is $\alpha_1 = 0$, $\alpha_2 = 0$, $\ldots$, $\alpha_k = 0$.

To do this, we first form the dot product of both sides of the equation with $\mathbf{v}_1$. This gives

$$\mathbf{v}_1 \cdot (\alpha_1 \mathbf{v}_1 + \alpha_2 \mathbf{v}_2 + \cdots + \alpha_k \mathbf{v}_k) = \mathbf{v}_1 \cdot \mathbf{0}.$$

Expanding the left-hand side gives

$$\alpha_1 (\mathbf{v}_1 \cdot \mathbf{v}_1) + \alpha_2 (\mathbf{v}_1 \cdot \mathbf{v}_2) + \cdots + \alpha_k (\mathbf{v}_1 \cdot \mathbf{v}_k) = \mathbf{v}_1 \cdot \mathbf{0}.$$

But $\{\mathbf{v}_1, \mathbf{v}_2, \ldots, \mathbf{v}_k\}$ is an orthogonal set, so

$$\mathbf{v}_1 \cdot \mathbf{v}_2 = 0, \quad \mathbf{v}_1 \cdot \mathbf{v}_3 = 0, \quad \ldots, \quad \mathbf{v}_1 \cdot \mathbf{v}_k = 0.$$

Since $\mathbf{v}_1 \cdot \mathbf{0} = 0$, it follows that

$$\alpha_1 (\mathbf{v}_1 \cdot \mathbf{v}_1) = 0.$$

But $\mathbf{v}_1 \cdot \mathbf{v}_1$ is non-zero, since $\mathbf{v}_1$ is a non-zero vector, so $\alpha_1 = 0$.

In the same way, forming the dot product of both sides of the equation with $\mathbf{v}_2$ yields $\alpha_2 = 0$, forming the dot product with $\mathbf{v}_3$ yields $\alpha_3 = 0$, and so on.

Thus $\alpha_1 = 0$, $\alpha_2 = 0$, $\ldots$, $\alpha_k = 0$, as required.   ■

Since any set of n linearly independent vectors in $\mathbb{R}^n$ forms a basis for $\mathbb{R}^n$, we obtain the following theorem which is a corollary to Theorem 5.1.

Theorem 5.2   Any orthogonal set of n non-zero vectors in $\mathbb{R}^n$ is an orthogonal basis for $\mathbb{R}^n$.

Exercise 5.5   Show that

$$\{(1, 2, 1, 0), (-1, 1, -1, 1), (1, 0, -1, 0), (1, -1, 1, 3)\}$$

is an orthogonal basis for $\mathbb{R}^4$.

Expressing vectors in terms of orthogonal bases

Given an orthogonal basis for $\mathbb{R}^n$, it is particularly easy to express any given vector as a linear combination of the basis vectors. As in the audio frames, we simply need to calculate dot products; we do not need to solve a system of linear equations.

Theorem 5.3   Let $\{\mathbf{v}_1, \mathbf{v}_2, \ldots, \mathbf{v}_n\}$ be an orthogonal basis for $\mathbb{R}^n$ and let $\mathbf{u}$ be any vector in $\mathbb{R}^n$. Then

$$\mathbf{u} = \left(\frac{\mathbf{v}_1 \cdot \mathbf{u}}{\mathbf{v}_1 \cdot \mathbf{v}_1} \right) \mathbf{v}_1 + \left(\frac{\mathbf{v}_2 \cdot \mathbf{u}}{\mathbf{v}_2 \cdot \mathbf{v}_2} \right) \mathbf{v}_2 + \cdots + \left(\frac{\mathbf{v}_n \cdot \mathbf{u}}{\mathbf{v}_n \cdot \mathbf{v}_n} \right) \mathbf{v}_n.$$

Proof   Let $\{\mathbf{v}_1, \mathbf{v}_2, \ldots, \mathbf{v}_n\}$ be an orthogonal basis for $\mathbb{R}^n$ and let $\mathbf{u}$ be any vector in $\mathbb{R}^n$. Since $\mathbf{u} \in \mathbb{R}^n$, we can write $\mathbf{u}$ as a linear combination of the basis vectors $\mathbf{v}_1, \mathbf{v}_2, \ldots, \mathbf{v}_n$:

$$\mathbf{u} = \alpha_1 \mathbf{v}_1 + \alpha_2 \mathbf{v}_2 + \cdots + \alpha_n \mathbf{v}_n. \tag{5.1}$$

Forming the dot product of both sides of equation (5.1) with $\mathbf{v}_1$ gives

$$\mathbf{v}_1 \cdot \mathbf{u} = \alpha_1 (\mathbf{v}_1 \cdot \mathbf{v}_1) \quad \text{(all other terms are 0),}$$

so $\alpha_1 = \dfrac{\mathbf{v}_1 \cdot \mathbf{u}}{\mathbf{v}_1 \cdot \mathbf{v}_1}$.

Similarly, forming the dot product of both sides of equation (5.1) with $\mathbf{v}_2$ gives

$$\mathbf{v}_2 \cdot \mathbf{u} = \alpha_2 (\mathbf{v}_2 \cdot \mathbf{v}_2) \quad \text{(all other terms are 0),}$$

so $\alpha_2 = \dfrac{\mathbf{v}_2 \cdot \mathbf{u}}{\mathbf{v}_2 \cdot \mathbf{v}_2}$.

Continuing in this way, we deduce that

$$\alpha_i = \dfrac{\mathbf{v}_i \cdot \mathbf{u}}{\mathbf{v}_i \cdot \mathbf{v}_i} \quad \text{for each } i = 1, 2, \ldots, n.$$

Thus

$$\mathbf{u} = \left(\dfrac{\mathbf{v}_1 \cdot \mathbf{u}}{\mathbf{v}_1 \cdot \mathbf{v}_1} \right) \mathbf{v}_1 + \left(\dfrac{\mathbf{v}_2 \cdot \mathbf{u}}{\mathbf{v}_2 \cdot \mathbf{v}_2} \right) \mathbf{v}_2 + \cdots + \left(\dfrac{\mathbf{v}_n \cdot \mathbf{u}}{\mathbf{v}_n \cdot \mathbf{v}_n} \right) \mathbf{v}_n,$$

as required. ∎

We can express the result of Theorem 5.3 in the form of a strategy.

Strategy 5.3   To express a vector $\mathbf{u}$ in terms of an orthogonal basis $\mathbf{v}_1, \mathbf{v}_2, \ldots, \mathbf{v}_n$.

1. Calculate $\alpha_1 = \dfrac{\mathbf{v}_1 \cdot \mathbf{u}}{\mathbf{v}_1 \cdot \mathbf{v}_1}, \; \alpha_2 = \dfrac{\mathbf{v}_2 \cdot \mathbf{u}}{\mathbf{v}_2 \cdot \mathbf{v}_2}, \; \ldots, \; \alpha_n = \dfrac{\mathbf{v}_n \cdot \mathbf{u}}{\mathbf{v}_n \cdot \mathbf{v}_n}$.

2. Write $\mathbf{u} = \alpha_1 \mathbf{v}_1 + \alpha_2 \mathbf{v}_2 + \cdots + \alpha_n \mathbf{v}_n$.

Strategy 5.3 is a generalisation of the strategy in Frame 6.

Exercise 5.6   Express the vector $(1, 2, 3, 4)$ in terms of the orthogonal basis for $\mathbb{R}^4$ in Exercise 5.5.

Extending orthogonal sets

In the audio section you saw how to extend a given orthogonal set of vectors in $\mathbb{R}^4$ to an orthogonal basis. In particular, to find an orthogonal basis containing the vector $(1, 2, -5, -1)$, we first wrote down the equation of a hyperplane orthogonal to this vector—namely $x + 2y - 5z - w = 0$. We then chose an arbitrary basis for this hyperplane and then adjusted it vector by vector to produce an orthogonal basis for $\mathbb{R}^4$.

See Frames 14 and 15.

This idea underlies the following method for constructing orthogonal bases, known as the *Gram–Schmidt orthogonalisation process*. In carrying out this method, we start with any basis and then adjust it vector by vector until the resulting basis is an orthogonal basis.

Theorem 5.4 Gram–Schmidt orthogonalisation process

Let $\{\mathbf{w}_1, \mathbf{w}_2, \ldots, \mathbf{w}_n\}$ be a basis for $\mathbb{R}^n$, and let

$$\mathbf{v}_1 = \mathbf{w}_1,$$

$$\mathbf{v}_2 = \mathbf{w}_2 - \left(\frac{\mathbf{v}_1 \cdot \mathbf{w}_2}{\mathbf{v}_1 \cdot \mathbf{v}_1}\right) \mathbf{v}_1,$$

$$\mathbf{v}_3 = \mathbf{w}_3 - \left(\frac{\mathbf{v}_1 \cdot \mathbf{w}_3}{\mathbf{v}_1 \cdot \mathbf{v}_1}\right) \mathbf{v}_1 - \left(\frac{\mathbf{v}_2 \cdot \mathbf{w}_3}{\mathbf{v}_2 \cdot \mathbf{v}_2}\right) \mathbf{v}_2,$$

$$\vdots$$

$$\mathbf{v}_n = \mathbf{w}_n - \left(\frac{\mathbf{v}_1 \cdot \mathbf{w}_n}{\mathbf{v}_1 \cdot \mathbf{v}_1}\right) \mathbf{v}_1 - \left(\frac{\mathbf{v}_2 \cdot \mathbf{w}_n}{\mathbf{v}_2 \cdot \mathbf{v}_2}\right) \mathbf{v}_2$$

$$- \cdots - \left(\frac{\mathbf{v}_{n-1} \cdot \mathbf{w}_n}{\mathbf{v}_{n-1} \cdot \mathbf{v}_{n-1}}\right) \mathbf{v}_{n-1}.$$

Then $\{\mathbf{v}_1, \mathbf{v}_2, \ldots, \mathbf{v}_n\}$ is an orthogonal basis for $\mathbb{R}^n$.

Proof   We note first that $\mathbf{v}_2$ is orthogonal to $\mathbf{v}_1$, since

$$\mathbf{v}_1 \cdot \mathbf{v}_2 = \mathbf{v}_1 \cdot \left(\mathbf{w}_2 - \left(\frac{\mathbf{v}_1 \cdot \mathbf{w}_2}{\mathbf{v}_1 \cdot \mathbf{v}_1}\right) \mathbf{v}_1\right)$$

$$= (\mathbf{v}_1 \cdot \mathbf{w}_2) - \left(\frac{\mathbf{v}_1 \cdot \mathbf{w}_2}{\mathbf{v}_1 \cdot \mathbf{v}_1}\right) (\mathbf{v}_1 \cdot \mathbf{v}_1)$$

$$= (\mathbf{v}_1 \cdot \mathbf{w}_2) - (\mathbf{v}_1 \cdot \mathbf{w}_2) = 0.$$

Next we note that $\mathbf{v}_3$ is orthogonal to both $\mathbf{v}_1$ and $\mathbf{v}_2$, since

$$\mathbf{v}_1 \cdot \mathbf{v}_3 = \mathbf{v}_1 \cdot \left(\mathbf{w}_3 - \left(\frac{\mathbf{v}_1 \cdot \mathbf{w}_3}{\mathbf{v}_1 \cdot \mathbf{v}_1}\right) \mathbf{v}_1 - \left(\frac{\mathbf{v}_2 \cdot \mathbf{w}_3}{\mathbf{v}_2 \cdot \mathbf{v}_2}\right) \mathbf{v}_2\right)$$

$$= (\mathbf{v}_1 \cdot \mathbf{w}_3) - \left(\frac{\mathbf{v}_1 \cdot \mathbf{w}_3}{\mathbf{v}_1 \cdot \mathbf{v}_1}\right) (\mathbf{v}_1 \cdot \mathbf{v}_1) - \left(\frac{\mathbf{v}_2 \cdot \mathbf{w}_3}{\mathbf{v}_2 \cdot \mathbf{v}_2}\right) (\mathbf{v}_1 \cdot \mathbf{v}_2)$$

$$= (\mathbf{v}_1 \cdot \mathbf{w}_3) - (\mathbf{v}_1 \cdot \mathbf{w}_3) - 0$$

$$= 0$$

because $\mathbf{v}_1$ and $\mathbf{v}_2$ are orthogonal.

Similarly,

$$\mathbf{v}_2 \cdot \mathbf{v}_3 = \mathbf{v}_2 \cdot \left(\mathbf{w}_3 - \left(\frac{\mathbf{v}_1 \cdot \mathbf{w}_3}{\mathbf{v}_1 \cdot \mathbf{v}_1}\right) \mathbf{v}_1 - \left(\frac{\mathbf{v}_2 \cdot \mathbf{w}_3}{\mathbf{v}_2 \cdot \mathbf{v}_2}\right) \mathbf{v}_2\right)$$

$$= (\mathbf{v}_2 \cdot \mathbf{w}_3) - \left(\frac{\mathbf{v}_1 \cdot \mathbf{w}_3}{\mathbf{v}_1 \cdot \mathbf{v}_1}\right) (\mathbf{v}_2 \cdot \mathbf{v}_1) - \left(\frac{\mathbf{v}_2 \cdot \mathbf{w}_3}{\mathbf{v}_2 \cdot \mathbf{v}_2}\right) (\mathbf{v}_2 \cdot \mathbf{v}_2)$$

$$= (\mathbf{v}_2 \cdot \mathbf{w}_3) - 0 - (\mathbf{v}_2 \cdot \mathbf{w}_3)$$

$$= 0.$$

Continuing in this way, we deduce that each of the vectors $\mathbf{v}_i$ is orthogonal to all the previous ones. It follows that $\mathbf{v}_i \cdot \mathbf{v}_j = 0$ for all i, j with $i \neq j$, and hence that $\{\mathbf{v}_1, \mathbf{v}_2, \ldots, \mathbf{v}_n\}$ is an orthogonal basis for $\mathbb{R}^n$.   ∎

Exercise 5.7   Apply the Gram–Schmidt orthogonalisation process to the following basis for $\mathbb{R}^5$:

$$\{(1, 2, 1, 0, 0), (-1, 1, -1, 1, 0), (0, 0, 0, 0, 1), (1, 0, 0, 0, 0), (0, 1, 0, 0, 0)\}.$$

Orthonormal bases

In Section 3 we stated that it is sometimes convenient to choose basis vectors along the major and minor axes of an ellipse. In many examples, it is also useful to require one further condition—that the basis vectors all have length 1, as in the standard basis.

In $\mathbb{R}^2$, the length of a vector $\mathbf{v} = (x, y)$ is given by

$$\|\mathbf{v}\| = \sqrt{\mathbf{v} \cdot \mathbf{v}} = \sqrt{x^2 + y^2}.$$

For example, if $\mathbf{v} = (5, -12)$, then $\|\mathbf{v}\| = \sqrt{5^2 + (-12)^2} = \sqrt{169} = 13$.

We can similarly define the lengths of vectors in $\mathbb{R}^n$, for any positive integer n.

Unit LA1, Section 3.

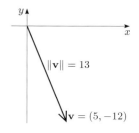

> **Definition**   Let $\mathbf{v} = (v_1, v_2, \ldots, v_n)$ be a vector in $\mathbb{R}^n$. Then the length of $\mathbf{v}$ is
>
> $$\|\mathbf{v}\| = \sqrt{\mathbf{v} \cdot \mathbf{v}} = \sqrt{v_1^2 + v_2^2 + \cdots + v_n^2}.$$

Exercise 5.8   Calculate the lengths of the following vectors.

(a) $(3, -4, 5)$ in $\mathbb{R}^3$.   (b) $(1, 2, -1, 0, 3)$ in $\mathbb{R}^5$.

Exercise 5.9   Prove that if $\mathbf{v}$ is any non-zero vector in $\mathbb{R}^n$, then $\mathbf{v}/\|\mathbf{v}\| = (1/\|\mathbf{v}\|)\mathbf{v}$ has length 1.

Now we make the following important definition.

> **Definition**   An **orthonormal basis** for $\mathbb{R}^n$ is an orthogonal basis in which each basis vector has length 1.

It follows from the result of Exercise 5.9 that, given an orthogonal basis for $\mathbb{R}^n$, we can obtain an orthonormal basis by scalar multiplying each basis vector by the reciprocal of its length. This leads to the following strategy for constructing an orthonormal basis.

> **Strategy 5.4**   To construct an orthonormal basis for $\mathbb{R}^n$ from an orthogonal basis $\{\mathbf{v}_1, \mathbf{v}_2, \ldots, \mathbf{v}_n\}$ for $\mathbb{R}^n$.
>
> 1.   Calculate the length of each basis vector.
>
> 2.   Divide each basis vector by its length.
>
> The required orthonormal basis is $\left\{ \dfrac{\mathbf{v}_1}{\|\mathbf{v}_1\|}, \dfrac{\mathbf{v}_2}{\|\mathbf{v}_2\|}, \ldots, \dfrac{\mathbf{v}_n}{\|\mathbf{v}_n\|} \right\}$.

For example, we can use Strategy 5.4 to obtain an orthonormal basis for $\mathbb{R}^3$ starting with the orthogonal basis $\{(2, 1, 1), (1, -4, 2), (-2, 1, 3)\}$, as follows.

We calculate the length of each basis vector:

$$\|(2, 1, 1)\| = \sqrt{2^2 + 1^2 + 1^2} = \sqrt{6},$$
$$\|(1, -4, 2)\| = \sqrt{1^2 + (-4)^2 + 2^2} = \sqrt{21},$$
$$\|(-2, 1, 3)\| = \sqrt{(-2)^2 + 1^2 + 3^2} = \sqrt{14}.$$

Dividing each orthogonal basis vector by its length, we obtain the orthonormal basis

$$\left\{ \frac{1}{\sqrt{6}}(2, 1, 1), \frac{1}{\sqrt{21}}(1, -4, 2), \frac{1}{\sqrt{14}}(-2, 1, 3) \right\}.$$

Exercise 5.10   Use the orthogonal basis in Exercise 5.5 to construct an orthonormal basis for $\mathbb{R}^4$.

Note that some of our earlier results become much simpler if we use an orthonormal basis, rather than an orthogonal one. For example, Theorem 5.3 takes the following form.

Theorem 5.5   Let $\{\mathbf{v}_1, \mathbf{v}_2, \ldots, \mathbf{v}_n\}$ be an orthonormal basis for $\mathbb{R}^n$, and let $\mathbf{u}$ be any vector in $\mathbb{R}^n$. Then

$$\mathbf{u} = (\mathbf{v}_1 \cdot \mathbf{u})\mathbf{v}_1 + (\mathbf{v}_2 \cdot \mathbf{u})\mathbf{v}_2 + \cdots + (\mathbf{v}_n \cdot \mathbf{u})\mathbf{v}_n.$$

Other vector spaces

We conclude this section by remarking that it is possible to define dot products in vector spaces other than $\mathbb{R}^n$. For example, in the vector space P_3, we can define the dot product of two polynomials p_1 and p_2 by

$$p_1 \cdot p_2 = \int_{-1}^{1} p_1(x)p_2(x)\, dx.$$

Such a dot product has properties that are very similar to those of the dot product in $\mathbb{R}^n$—for example, $p_1 \cdot p_2 = p_2 \cdot p_1$ for any polynomials p_1 and p_2.

We can then define such concepts as *orthogonal polynomials*, the *length of a polynomial*, and the *distance and angle between two polynomials*. For example, the polynomials $p_1(x) = x$ and $p_2(x) = x^2$ are orthogonal, since

$$p_1 \cdot p_2 = \int_{-1}^{1} x \cdot x^2 \, dx = \left[\tfrac{1}{4}x^4 \right]_{-1}^{1} = 0$$

and the length of p_2 is given by

$$\|p_2\|^2 = p_2 \cdot p_2 = \int_{-1}^{1} x^2 \cdot x^2 \, dx = \left[\tfrac{1}{5}x^5 \right]_{-1}^{1} = \tfrac{2}{5},$$

so $\|p_2\| = \sqrt{\tfrac{2}{5}}$.

Although such concepts may seem at first sight to make little sense intuitively, they have proved to be of great interest and importance, for example in mathematical physics. They also show that the mathematical structures we have introduced are valid in a wide range of contexts.

Further exercises

Exercise 5.11   Let $\mathbf{v}_1 = (1, 5, -3, 4, -7)$ and $\mathbf{v}_2 = (2, 8, 0, -7, -2)$ be vectors in $\mathbb{R}^5$.

(a) Calculate the dot product $\mathbf{v}_1 \cdot \mathbf{v}_2$.

(b) Determine the lengths of $\mathbf{v}_1$ and $\mathbf{v}_2$.

Exercise 5.12

(a) Verify that

$$\{(5, 5, 5, 5), (5, -5, -5, 5), (5, 0, 0, -5), (0, 5, -5, 0)\}$$

is an orthogonal basis for $\mathbb{R}^4$.

(b) Express the vector $(5, 0, 0, 0)$ as a linear combination of the basis vectors in part (a).

(c) Determine the corresponding orthonormal basis for $\mathbb{R}^4$.

Exercise 5.13

(a) Choose a basis for $\mathbb{R}^3$ containing the vector $(1, -2, 2)$, and apply the Gram–Schmidt orthogonalisation process to find an orthogonal basis for $\mathbb{R}^3$ containing the vector $(1, -2, 2)$.

(b) Determine the corresponding orthonormal basis for $\mathbb{R}^3$.

Exercise 5.14   Starting with the basis

$$\{(2, 2, 1, 0), (1, 2, 0, 2), (0, 1, 2, 2), (2, 0, 2, 1)\}$$

for $\mathbb{R}^4$, use the Gram–Schmidt orthogonalisation process to find an orthogonal basis for the hyperplane $2x + 2y + z = 0$.

Solutions to the exercises

1.1 $\mathbf{u} + \mathbf{v} = (1, -1, 2, 0, -3) + (0, 2, -1, 4, 0)$
$$= (1, 1, 1, 4, -3),$$
$-3\mathbf{u} = -3(1, -1, 2, 0, -3) = (-3, 3, -6, 0, 9).$

1.2 (a) $\mathbf{u} + \mathbf{v} = (u_1, u_2, u_3, u_4) + (v_1, v_2, v_3, v_4)$
$$= (u_1 + v_1, u_2 + v_2, u_3 + v_3, u_4 + v_4)$$
$$= (v_1 + u_1, v_2 + u_2, v_3 + u_3, v_4 + u_4)$$
$$= (v_1, v_2, v_3, v_4) + (u_1, u_2, u_3, u_4)$$
$$= \mathbf{v} + \mathbf{u}$$

(b) $(\mathbf{u} + \mathbf{v}) + \mathbf{w}$
$$= ((u_1, u_2, u_3, u_4) + (v_1, v_2, v_3, v_4))$$
$$\quad + (w_1, w_2, w_3, w_4)$$
$$= (u_1 + v_1, u_2 + v_2, u_3 + v_3, u_4 + v_4)$$
$$\quad + (w_1, w_2, w_3, w_4)$$
$$= (u_1 + v_1 + w_1, u_2 + v_2 + w_2, u_3 + v_3 + w_3,$$
$$\quad u_4 + v_4 + w_4),$$
$\mathbf{u} + (\mathbf{v} + \mathbf{w})$
$$= (u_1, u_2, u_3, u_4)$$
$$\quad + ((v_1, v_2, v_3, v_4) + (w_1, w_2, w_3, w_4))$$
$$= (u_1, u_2, u_3, u_4)$$
$$\quad + (v_1 + w_1, v_2 + w_2, v_3 + w_3, v_4 + w_4)$$
$$= (u_1 + v_1 + w_1, u_2 + v_2 + w_2, u_3 + v_3 + w_3,$$
$$\quad u_4 + v_4 + w_4).$$
Therefore
$$(\mathbf{u} + \mathbf{v}) + \mathbf{w} = \mathbf{u} + (\mathbf{v} + \mathbf{w}).$$

(c) $\mathbf{v} + \mathbf{0} = (v_1, v_2, v_3, v_4) + (0, 0, 0, 0)$
$$= (v_1 + 0, v_2 + 0, v_3 + 0, v_4 + 0)$$
$$= (v_1, v_2, v_3, v_4) = \mathbf{v}$$
Also using part (a), we have
$$\mathbf{v} + \mathbf{0} = \mathbf{0} + \mathbf{v} = \mathbf{v}.$$

(d) $\mathbf{v} + (-\mathbf{v}) = (v_1, v_2, v_3, v_4) + (-v_1, -v_2, -v_3, -v_4)$
$$= (v_1 - v_1, v_2 - v_2, v_3 - v_3, v_4 - v_4)$$
$$= (0, 0, 0, 0) = \mathbf{0}$$

1.3 (a) $p_1(x) + p_2(x)$
$$= (a_1 + b_1 x + c_1 x^2) + (a_2 + b_2 x + c_2 x^2)$$
$$= (a_1 + a_2) + (b_1 + b_2)x + (c_1 + c_2)x^2$$
$$= (a_2 + a_1) + (b_2 + b_1)x + (c_2 + c_1)x^2$$
$$= (a_2 + b_2 x + c_2 x^2) + (a_1 + b_1 x + c_1 x^2)$$
$$= p_2(x) + p_1(x)$$

(b) $(p_1(x) + p_2(x)) + p_3(x)$
$$= ((a_1 + b_1 x + c_1 x^2) + (a_2 + b_2 x + c_2 x^2))$$
$$\quad + (a_3 + b_3 x + c_3 x^2)$$
$$= ((a_1 + a_2) + (b_1 + b_2)x + (c_1 + c_2)x^2)$$
$$\quad + (a_3 + b_3 x + c_3 x^2)$$
$$= (a_1 + a_2 + a_3) + (b_1 + b_2 + b_3)x$$
$$\quad + (c_1 + c_2 + c_3)x^2$$
and
$$p_1(x) + (p_2(x) + p_3(x))$$
$$= (a_1 + b_1 x + c_1 x^2)$$
$$\quad + ((a_2 + b_2 x + c_2 x^2) + (a_3 + b_3 x + c_3 x^2))$$
$$= (a_1 + b_1 x + c_1 x^2)$$
$$\quad + ((a_2 + a_3) + (b_2 + b_3)x + (c_2 + c_3)x^2)$$
$$= (a_1 + a_2 + a_3) + (b_1 + b_2 + b_3)x$$
$$\quad + (c_1 + c_2 + c_3)x^2.$$
Therefore
$$(p_1(x) + p_2(x)) + p_3(x)$$
$$= p_1(x) + (p_2(x) + p_3(x)).$$

(c) $p_1(x) + \mathbf{0} = (a_1 + b_1 x + c_1 x^2) + (0 + 0x + 0x^2)$
$$= (a_1 + 0) + (b_1 + 0)x + (c_1 + 0)x^2$$
$$= a_1 + b_1 x + c_1 x^2 = p_1(x)$$
Also using part (a), we have
$$p_1(x) + \mathbf{0} = \mathbf{0} + p_1(x) = p_1(x).$$

(d) $p_1(x) + (-p_1(x))$
$$= (a_1 + b_1 x + c_1 x^2) + (-a_1 - b_1 x - c_1 x^2)$$
$$= (a_1 - a_1) + (b_1 - b_1)x + (c_1 - c_1)x^2$$
$$= 0 + 0x + 0x^2 = \mathbf{0}$$

1.4 (a) $1 \times p(x) = 1 \times (1 - x + 2x^2)$
$$= 1 \times 1 - 1 \times x + 1 \times 2x^2$$
$$= 1 - x + 2x^2 = p(x)$$

(b) $\alpha(\beta p(x)) = 2(-3(1 - x + 2x^2))$
$$= 2(-3 + 3x - 6x^2)$$
$$= -6 + 6x - 12x^2$$
$$= -6(1 - x + 2x^2) = (\alpha\beta)p(x)$$

1.5 (a) The set of all ordered pairs (x, y) with $y = 2x + 1$ fails to satisfy A1. A counter-example for A1 is given by $\mathbf{u} = (1, 3)$ and $\mathbf{v} = (2, 5)$. Then $\mathbf{u} + \mathbf{v} = (1, 3) + (2, 5) = (3, 8)$, which does not belong to the set, since $2 \times 3 + 1 = 7 \neq 8$. So the set is not closed under vector addition.

The other axioms which fail are A2, A3 and S1.

(b) The set of matrices of the form $\begin{pmatrix} 0 & a \\ b & c \end{pmatrix}$ with $a, b, c \in \mathbb{Z}$ fails to satisfy S1. A counter-example for S1 is given by $\mathbf{A} = \begin{pmatrix} 0 & 2 \\ -1 & 3 \end{pmatrix}$ and $\alpha = \frac{1}{2}$. Then

$\alpha \mathbf{A} = \begin{pmatrix} 0 & 1 \\ -\frac{1}{2} & \frac{3}{2} \end{pmatrix}$, which does not belong to the set.

Also S2, D1 and D2 are meaningless because S1 fails.

1.6 (a) V fails to satisfy A1.

A counter-example is given by $p_1(x) = 2 + a_1 x$, $p_2(x) = 2 + a_2 x$. Then

$$p_1(x) + p_2(x) = (2 + a_1 x) + (2 + a_2 x)$$
$$= 4 + (a_1 + a_2)x.$$

This does not belong to V, so V is not closed under vector addition.

(b) V fails to satisfy A1.

A counter-example is given by $\mathbf{u} = (1, 1, -1)$, $\mathbf{v} = (0, -1, -4)$, which belong to V. Then

$$\mathbf{u} + \mathbf{v} = (1, 1, -1) + (0, -1, -4) = (1, 0, -5).$$

This does not belong to V, since

$$1 + 0 - 3 = -2 \neq -5,$$

so V is not closed under vector addition.

(c) V fails to satisfy S1.

A counter-example is given by $\mathbf{u} = (1, 2)$ and $\alpha = -2$. Then $\mathbf{u} \in V$, but $-2\mathbf{u} = (-2, -4)$ does not belong to V, since $-2 < 0$. So V is not closed under scalar multiplication.

(d) V fails to satisfy A1.

A counter-example is given by

$$\mathbf{A} = \begin{pmatrix} 1 & 0 \\ 0 & 1 \end{pmatrix}, \quad \mathbf{B} = \begin{pmatrix} 2 & 1 \\ 1 & 1 \end{pmatrix}.$$

Then $\mathbf{A}, \mathbf{B} \in V$, but

$$\mathbf{A} + \mathbf{B} = \begin{pmatrix} 3 & 1 \\ 1 & 2 \end{pmatrix}$$

has determinant 5, and so does not belong to V. Thus V is not closed under vector addition.

2.1 (a) $4\mathbf{v}_1 - 2\mathbf{v}_2 = 4(0, 3) - 2(2, 1)$
$$= (0, 12) - (4, 2) = (-4, 10)$$

(b) $3\mathbf{v}_1 + 2\mathbf{v}_2 = 3(1, 2, 1, 3) + 2(2, 1, 0, -1)$
$$= (3, 6, 3, 9) + (4, 2, 0, -2) = (7, 8, 3, 7)$$

2.2 (a) $2\mathbf{v}_1 - 4\mathbf{v}_2 = 2(2 - x + 3x^2) - 4(-1 + x)$
$= (4 - 2x + 6x^2) - (-4 + 4x) = 8 - 6x + 6x^2$

(b) $2\mathbf{v}_1 - 4\mathbf{v}_2 = 2\sin x - 4x\cos x$

(c) $2\mathbf{v}_1 - 4\mathbf{v}_2 = 2\begin{pmatrix} -1 & 1 \\ 2 & 0 \end{pmatrix} - 4\begin{pmatrix} 3 & 1 \\ 0 & -2 \end{pmatrix}$

$= \begin{pmatrix} -2 & 2 \\ 4 & 0 \end{pmatrix} - \begin{pmatrix} 12 & 4 \\ 0 & -8 \end{pmatrix} = \begin{pmatrix} -14 & -2 \\ 4 & 8 \end{pmatrix}$

2.3 We use Strategy 2.1.

(a) Let α and β be real numbers such that
$$(2, 4) = \alpha(0, 3) + \beta(2, 1) = (2\beta, 3\alpha + \beta).$$
Equating corresponding coordinates, we obtain the simultaneous equations
$$\begin{cases} 2\beta = 2, \\ 3\alpha + \beta = 4. \end{cases}$$
The first equation gives $\beta = 1$, and substituting this into the second equation gives $\alpha = 1$, so
$$(2, 4) = (0, 3) + (2, 1).$$

(b) Let α, β and γ be real numbers such that
$$(2, 3, -2) = \alpha(0, 1, 0) + \beta(1, 2, -1) + \gamma(1, 1, -2)$$
$$= (\beta + \gamma, \alpha + 2\beta + \gamma, -\beta - 2\gamma).$$
Equating corresponding coordinates, we obtain the simultaneous equations
$$\begin{cases} \beta + \gamma = 2, \\ \alpha + 2\beta + \gamma = 3, \\ -\beta - 2\gamma = -2. \end{cases}$$
Adding the first and third equations gives $\gamma = 0$, and substituting this into the first equation gives $\beta = 2$. Substituting both these values into the second equation gives $\alpha = -1$, so
$$(2, 3, -2) = -(0, 1, 0) + 2(1, 2, -1) + 0(1, 1, -2).$$

(c) Let α and β be real numbers such that
$$\begin{pmatrix} 3 & 1 \\ 0 & 4 \end{pmatrix} = \alpha\begin{pmatrix} 1 & -1 \\ 0 & 2 \end{pmatrix} + \beta\begin{pmatrix} 0 & -2 \\ 0 & 1 \end{pmatrix}$$
$$= \begin{pmatrix} \alpha & -\alpha - 2\beta \\ 0 & 2\alpha + \beta \end{pmatrix}.$$
Equating corresponding entries, we obtain the simultaneous equations
$$\begin{cases} \alpha = 3, \\ -\alpha - 2\beta = 1, \\ 2\alpha + \beta = 4. \end{cases}$$
The first equation gives $\alpha = 3$, and substituting this into the second equation gives $\beta = -2$. These values also satisfy the third equation, so
$$\begin{pmatrix} 3 & 1 \\ 0 & 4 \end{pmatrix} = 3\begin{pmatrix} 1 & -1 \\ 0 & 2 \end{pmatrix} - 2\begin{pmatrix} 0 & -2 \\ 0 & 1 \end{pmatrix}.$$

2.4 (a) We write
$$(1, 5, 4) = \alpha\mathbf{v}_1 + \beta\mathbf{v}_2$$
$$= \alpha(1, 0, 3) + \beta(0, 2, 0) = (\alpha, 2\beta, 3\alpha).$$
Equating corresponding coordinates gives the simultaneous equations
$$\begin{cases} \alpha = 1, \\ 2\beta = 5, \\ 3\alpha = 4. \end{cases}$$
This system is inconsistent and therefore has no solution. So $(1, 5, 4)$ does not belong to $\langle\{\mathbf{v}_1, \mathbf{v}_2\}\rangle$.

(b) We write
$$(1,5,4) = \alpha\mathbf{v}_1 + \beta\mathbf{v}_2 + \gamma\mathbf{v}_3$$
$$= \alpha(1,0,3) + \beta(0,2,0) + \gamma(0,3,1)$$
$$= (\alpha, 2\beta + 3\gamma, 3\alpha + \gamma).$$

Equating corresponding coordinates gives the simultaneous equations
$$\begin{cases} \alpha & = 1, \\ 2\beta + 3\gamma = 5, \\ 3\alpha \quad + \gamma = 4. \end{cases}$$

The first equation gives $\alpha = 1$, and substituting this into the third gives $\gamma = 1$. Substituting this into the second equation gives $\beta = 1$, so $(1,5,4)$ belongs to $\langle\{\mathbf{v}_1, \mathbf{v}_2, \mathbf{v}_3\}\rangle$; it can be written as
$$(1,5,4) = 1(1,0,3) + 1(0,2,0) + 1(0,3,1).$$

2.5 (a) We write
$$(x,y) = \alpha(1,1) + \beta(-1,2) = (\alpha - \beta, \alpha + 2\beta).$$

Equating corresponding coordinates gives the simultaneous equations
$$\begin{cases} \alpha - \beta = x, \\ \alpha + 2\beta = y. \end{cases}$$

These equations have solution $\alpha = \frac{1}{3}(2x + y)$ and $\beta = \frac{1}{3}(y - x)$, so any vector in $\mathbb{R}^2$ can be written in terms of $(1,1)$ and $(-1,2)$ as
$$(x,y) = \frac{1}{3}(2x + y)(1,1) + \frac{1}{3}(y - x)(-1,2).$$

So $\{(1,1), (-1,2)\}$ is a spanning set for $\mathbb{R}^2$.

(b) We write
$$(x,y) = \alpha(2,-1) + \beta(3,2)$$
$$= (2\alpha + 3\beta, -\alpha + 2\beta).$$

Equating corresponding coordinates gives the simultaneous equations
$$\begin{cases} 2\alpha + 3\beta = x, \\ -\alpha + 2\beta = y. \end{cases}$$

These equations have solution $\alpha = \frac{1}{7}(2x - 3y)$ and $\beta = \frac{1}{7}(x + 2y)$, so any vector in $\mathbb{R}^2$ can be written in terms of $(2,-1)$ and $(3,2)$ as
$$(x,y) = \frac{1}{7}(2x - 3y)(2,-1) + \frac{1}{7}(x + 2y)(3,2).$$

So $\{(2,-1), (3,2)\}$ is a spanning set for $\mathbb{R}^2$.

2.6 We write
$$(x,y,z) = \alpha(1,0,0) + \beta(1,1,0) + \gamma(2,0,1)$$
$$= (\alpha + \beta + 2\gamma, \beta, \gamma).$$

Equating corresponding coordinates gives the simultaneous equations
$$\begin{cases} \alpha + \beta + 2\gamma = x, \\ \beta \quad = y, \\ \gamma = z. \end{cases}$$

Working backwards from the third equation, we find that these equations have solution $\gamma = z$, $\beta = y$ and $\alpha = x - y - 2z$, so any vector in $\mathbb{R}^3$ can be written in terms of $(1,0,0)$, $(1,1,0)$ and $(2,0,1)$ as
$$(x,y,z) = (x - y - 2z)(1,0,0) + y(1,1,0) + z(2,0,1).$$

So $\{(1,0,0), (1,1,0), (2,0,1)\}$ is a spanning set for $\mathbb{R}^3$.

2.7 Each polynomial in P_4 can be written as $a + bx + cx^2 + dx^3$. To show that $a + bx + cx^2 + dx^3$ belongs to $\langle\{1 + x, 1 + x^2, 1 + x^3, x\}\rangle$, we write
$$a + bx + cx^2 + dx^3$$
$$= \alpha(1 + x) + \beta(1 + x^2) + \gamma(1 + x^3) + \delta x$$
$$= (\alpha + \beta + \gamma) + (\alpha + \delta)x + \beta x^2 + \gamma x^3.$$

Equating corresponding coefficients gives the simultaneous equations
$$\begin{cases} \alpha + \beta + \gamma \quad = a, \\ \alpha \quad\quad + \delta = b, \\ \beta \quad = c, \\ \gamma \quad = d. \end{cases}$$

These have solution $\gamma = d$, $\beta = c$, $\alpha = a - c - d$ and $\delta = b - a + c + d$. So
$$a + bx + cx^2 + dx^3$$
$$= (a - c - d)(1 + x) + c(1 + x^2) + d(1 + x^3)$$
$$+ (b - a + c + d)x.$$

Thus $\langle\{1 + x, 1 + x^2, 1 + x^3, x\}\rangle = P_4$.

2.8 (a) We have
$$\langle S\rangle = \{\alpha(1,0,0) : \alpha \in \mathbb{R}\} = \{(\alpha, 0, 0) : \alpha \in \mathbb{R}\}.$$
(Geometrically, $\langle S\rangle$ is the x-axis.)

(b) We have
$$\langle S\rangle = \left\{ \alpha\begin{pmatrix} 2 & 0 \\ 0 & 3 \end{pmatrix} + \beta\begin{pmatrix} -1 & 0 \\ 0 & 2 \end{pmatrix} : \alpha, \beta \in \mathbb{R} \right\}$$
$$= \left\{ \begin{pmatrix} 2\alpha - \beta & 0 \\ 0 & 3\alpha + 2\beta \end{pmatrix} : \alpha, \beta \in \mathbb{R} \right\}.$$

Thus
$$\langle S\rangle \subseteq \left\{ \begin{pmatrix} a & 0 \\ 0 & b \end{pmatrix} : a, b \in \mathbb{R} \right\}.$$

In fact, every 2×2 diagonal matrix belongs to $\langle S\rangle$. To show this, we write
$$\begin{pmatrix} a & 0 \\ 0 & b \end{pmatrix} = \begin{pmatrix} 2\alpha - \beta & 0 \\ 0 & 3\alpha + 2\beta \end{pmatrix},$$
and equate corresponding entries to give the simultaneous equations
$$\begin{cases} 2\alpha - \beta = a, \\ 3\alpha + 2\beta = b. \end{cases}$$

These have solution $\alpha = \frac{1}{7}(2a + b)$ and $\beta = \frac{1}{7}(-3a + 2b)$, so
$$\begin{pmatrix} a & 0 \\ 0 & b \end{pmatrix} \in \langle S\rangle.$$

Hence
$$\langle S\rangle = \left\{ \begin{pmatrix} a & 0 \\ 0 & b \end{pmatrix} : a, b \in \mathbb{R} \right\}.$$

2.9 **(a)** $2\mathbf{u} - \mathbf{v} = 2(3, -1) - (2, 4)$
$$= (6, -2) - (2, 4) = (4, -6)$$

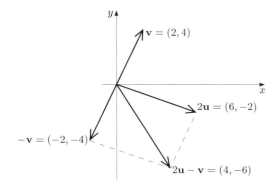

(b) $2\mathbf{u} - \mathbf{v} = (2, 4, 0) - (0, -1, \frac{3}{4}) = (2, 5, -\frac{3}{4})$

2.10 **(a)** $2\mathbf{u} - \mathbf{v} + 3\mathbf{w}$
$$= 2(1, 0, 1) - (-1, 1, 0) + 3(0, 0, 1)$$
$$= (2, 0, 2) - (-1, 1, 0) + (0, 0, 3)$$
$$= (3, -1, 5)$$

(b) $\alpha\mathbf{u} + \beta\mathbf{v} + \gamma\mathbf{w}$
$$= \alpha(1, 0, 1) + \beta(-1, 1, 0) + \gamma(0, 0, 1)$$
$$= (\alpha - \beta, \beta, \alpha + \gamma) = (0, 1, 0)$$

Equating corresponding coordinates, we obtain the simultaneous equations
$$\begin{cases} \alpha - \beta & = 0, \\ \beta & = 1, \\ \alpha & + \gamma = 0. \end{cases}$$
Solving these equations gives $\alpha = \beta = 1$ and $\gamma = -1$.

(c) From part (b), the only possibility is $\alpha = \beta = 1$. But $\mathbf{u} + \mathbf{v} = (0, 1, 1) \neq (0, 1, 0)$. So there do not exist any suitable α and β.

(d) $\alpha\mathbf{u} + \beta\mathbf{v} + \gamma\mathbf{w} + \delta\mathbf{z}$
$$= \alpha(1, 0, 1) + \beta(-1, 1, 0) + \gamma(0, 0, 1) + \delta(1, 1, 0)$$
$$= (\alpha - \beta + \delta, \beta + \delta, \alpha + \gamma) = (0, 1, 0).$$

Equating corresponding coordinates, we obtain the simultaneous equations
$$\begin{cases} \alpha - \beta & + \delta = 0, \\ \beta & + \delta = 1, \\ \alpha & + \gamma = 0. \end{cases}$$
Solving these equations, we let δ be any real number k. Then we find
$$\beta = 1 - k, \ \alpha = 1 - 2k, \ \gamma = -1 + 2k.$$
The general solution is
$$\alpha = 1 - 2k, \ \beta = 1 - k, \ \gamma = -1 + 2k, \ \delta = k,$$
for any real number k.

(There are other forms of this solution if you let one of the other coefficients equal k, but they are all equivalent.)

2.11 **(a)** We use Strategy 2.1.
We write
$$(0, 0, 1) = \alpha(1, 1, 0) + \beta(0, 1, 1) = (\alpha, \alpha + \beta, \beta).$$
Equating corresponding coordinates gives
$$\begin{cases} \alpha & = 0, \\ \alpha + \beta & = 0, \\ \beta & = 1. \end{cases}$$
These equations are inconsistent and therefore have no solution, so $(0, 0, 1)$ does not lie in the span of S.
Solving a similar set of equations gives
$$(4, 2, -2) = 4(1, 1, 0) - 2(0, 1, 1),$$
so $(4, 2, -2)$ lies in the span of S.

(b) The vectors in $\langle S \rangle$ are those of the form
$$\alpha(1, 1, 0) + \beta(0, 1, 1) = (\alpha, \alpha + \beta, \beta),$$
for $\alpha, \beta \in \mathbb{R}$. Thus the span $\langle S \rangle$ consists of all vectors in $\mathbb{R}^3$ whose middle coordinate is the sum of the other two.
Geometrically, $\langle S \rangle$ is the plane $x - y + z = 0$.

2.12 **(a)** We have
$$\langle S \rangle = \{\alpha(2, -1) : \alpha \in \mathbb{R}\} = \{(2\alpha, -\alpha) : \alpha \in \mathbb{R}\}.$$
Thus all points of $\langle S \rangle$ lie on the line $y = -\frac{1}{2}x$, and all points on the line are of this form. So $\langle S \rangle$ is the line $y = -\frac{1}{2}x$.

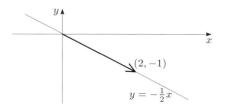

(b) We have
$$\langle S \rangle = \{\alpha(0, -1, 1) + \beta(0, 2, -3) : \alpha, \beta \in \mathbb{R}\}$$
$$= \{(0, -\alpha + 2\beta, \alpha - 3\beta) : \alpha, \beta \in \mathbb{R}\}.$$
Thus $\langle S \rangle$ is a subset of the (y, z)-plane.
By solving the simultaneous equations
$$\begin{cases} -\alpha + 2\beta = y, \\ \alpha - 3\beta = z, \end{cases}$$
we see that every point $(0, y, z)$ of the (y, z)-plane belongs to $\langle S \rangle$. Thus $\langle S \rangle$ is the (y, z)-plane.

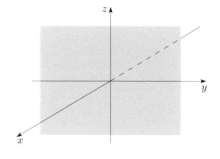

2.13 (a) A vector $p(x)$ lies in the span of $\{1 + 2x\}$ if and only if $p(x) = \alpha(1 + 2x)$. So $\langle S \rangle$ is the set of all vectors of the form $\alpha + 2\alpha x$, for some $\alpha \in \mathbb{R}$:

$$\langle S \rangle = \{\alpha + 2\alpha x : \alpha \in \mathbb{R}\}.$$

(b) A matrix $\mathbf{A}$ lies in the span of S if and only if

$$\mathbf{A} = \alpha \begin{pmatrix} 1 & 0 \\ 0 & 0 \end{pmatrix} + \beta \begin{pmatrix} 0 & 0 \\ 0 & 3 \end{pmatrix} = \begin{pmatrix} \alpha & 0 \\ 0 & 3\beta \end{pmatrix},$$

where $\alpha, \beta \in \mathbb{R}$. Thus

$$\langle S \rangle = \left\{ \begin{pmatrix} \alpha & 0 \\ 0 & 3\beta \end{pmatrix} : \alpha, \beta \in \mathbb{R} \right\}.$$

This is the set of all diagonal matrices in $M_{2,2}$.

2.14 Each vector in $\mathbb{R}^2$ can be written as (x, y). To show that $\{(-1, 0), (2, 1)\}$ spans $\mathbb{R}^2$, we must find α and β such that

$$(x, y) = \alpha(-1, 0) + \beta(2, 1)$$
$$= (-\alpha, 0) + (2\beta, \beta) = (-\alpha + 2\beta, \beta).$$

Equating corresponding coordinates gives the simultaneous equations

$$\begin{cases} -\alpha + 2\beta = x, \\ \beta = y, \end{cases}$$

whose solution is $\alpha = -x + 2y$, $\beta = y$. So any vector (x, y) in $\mathbb{R}^2$ can be written in terms of $(-1, 0)$ and $(2, 1)$ as

$$(x, y) = (-x + 2y)(-1, 0) + y(2, 1).$$

So $\{(-1, 0), (2, 1)\}$ spans $\mathbb{R}^2$.

3.1 (a) These two vectors are linearly independent because neither is a multiple of the other. (In this case there is no need to use Strategy 3.1.)

(b) Using Strategy 3.1, we write

$$\alpha(1, -1) + \beta(1, 1) + \gamma(2, 1) = (0, 0).$$

This gives the equations

$$\begin{cases} \alpha + \beta + 2\gamma = 0, \\ -\alpha + \beta + \gamma = 0. \end{cases}$$

Adding the equations gives $2\beta + 3\gamma = 0$, or $\beta = -\frac{3}{2}\gamma$, and substituting this into the first equation gives $\alpha = -\frac{1}{2}\gamma$. Letting $\gamma = 2$ gives $\alpha = -1$ and $\beta = -3$, so we can find α, β and γ not all zero, so the set $\{(1, -1), (1, 1), (2, 1)\}$ is linearly dependent.

(c) These two vectors are linearly independent because neither is a multiple of the other. (In this case there is no need to use Strategy 3.1.)

(d) We write

$$\alpha(1, 0, 0) + \beta(1, 1, 0) + \gamma(1, 1, 1) = (0, 0, 0).$$

This gives the equations

$$\begin{cases} \alpha + \beta + \gamma = 0, \\ \beta + \gamma = 0, \\ \gamma = 0. \end{cases}$$

The third equation gives $\gamma = 0$, and substituting into the second equation gives $\beta = 0$.

Finally, substituting into the first equation gives $\alpha = 0$. So the set $\{(1, 0, 0), (1, 1, 0), (1, 1, 1)\}$ is linearly independent.

(e) These two vectors are linearly independent because neither is a multiple of the other. (Again, there is no need to use Strategy 3.1.)

3.2 (a) The set $\{1, x, x^2, x^3, 1 + x + x^2 + x^3\}$ is linearly dependent because the fifth vector is the sum of the first four vectors. So

$$1 + x + x^2 + x^3 - (1 + x + x^2 + x^3) = 0.$$

(b) The set S is linearly independent because neither matrix is a multiple of the other.

(c) The set $\{1 + i, 1 - i\}$ is linearly independent because neither vector is a (real) multiple of the other.

3.3 (a) This set of vectors is not a basis for $\mathbb{R}^3$ because it does not span $\mathbb{R}^3$. Because none of the vectors has a non-zero x-component, we cannot write (x, y, z) in terms of these three vectors if $x \neq 0$, so the vectors do not span $\mathbb{R}^3$.

(b) We check both conditions in Strategy 3.2. First we use Strategy 3.1 for checking linear independence. Suppose that

$$\alpha(1, 2, 1) + \beta(1, 0, -1) + \gamma(0, 3, 1) = (0, 0, 0),$$

that is,

$$(\alpha + \beta, 2\alpha + 3\gamma, \alpha - \beta + \gamma) = (0, 0, 0).$$

Equating corresponding coordinates, we see that α, β and γ satisfy the simultaneous equations

$$\begin{cases} \alpha + \beta = 0, \\ 2\alpha + 3\gamma = 0, \\ \alpha - \beta + \gamma = 0. \end{cases}$$

Adding the third equation to the first gives $2\alpha + \gamma = 0$, and subtracting this from the second equation gives $\gamma = 0$. Substituting this into the second equation gives $\alpha = 0$. Finally, substituting $\alpha = 0$ into the first equation gives $\beta = 0$, so the set is linearly independent.

Next we check whether each vector in $\mathbb{R}^3$ can be written as a linear combination of the vectors in the set. Choosing (x, y, z) as an arbitrary vector in $\mathbb{R}^3$, we seek numbers α, β and γ such that

$$(x, y, z) = \alpha(1, 2, 1) + \beta(1, 0, -1) + \gamma(0, 3, 1).$$

Equating corresponding coordinates, we see that α, β and γ satisfy the simultaneous equations

$$\begin{cases} \alpha + \beta = x, \\ 2\alpha + 3\gamma = y, \\ \alpha - \beta + \gamma = z. \end{cases}$$

Adding the third equation to the first gives $2\alpha + \gamma = x + z$, and subtracting this from the second equation gives $\gamma = \frac{1}{2}(y - x - z)$. Substituting this into the second equation gives $\alpha = \frac{1}{4}(3x - y + 3z)$.

Finally, substituting for α in the first equation gives $\beta = \frac{1}{4}(x + y - 3z)$. So

$$(x, y, z) = \frac{1}{4}(3x - y + 3z)(1, 2, 1)$$
$$+ \frac{1}{4}(x + y - 3z)(1, 0, -1)$$
$$+ \frac{1}{2}(y - x - z)(0, 3, 1),$$

and the set of vectors spans $\mathbb{R}^3$.

Thus $\{(1, 2, 1), (1, 0, -1), (0, 3, 1)\}$ is a basis for $\mathbb{R}^3$.

(c) The set $\{(1, 0, 0), (0, 1, 0), (0, 0, 1), (1, 1, 1)\}$ is not a basis for $\mathbb{R}^3$ because it is not linearly independent; for example,

$$(1, 1, 1) = (1, 0, 0) + (0, 1, 0) + (0, 0, 1).$$

3.4 We check both conditions in Strategy 3.2.

This set is linearly independent because there are only two vectors in the set, and neither vector is a multiple of the other.

Next we check whether each vector in $\mathbb{R}^4$ can be written as a linear combination of the vectors in the set. Choosing (x, y, z, w) as an arbitrary vector in $\mathbb{R}^4$, we seek numbers α and β such that

$$(x, y, z, w) = \alpha(1, 2, -1, -1) + \beta(-1, 5, 1, 3).$$

Equating corresponding coordinates, we see that α and β satisfy the simultaneous equations

$$\begin{cases} \alpha - \beta = x, \\ 2\alpha + 5\beta = y, \\ -\alpha + \beta = z, \\ -\alpha + 3\beta = w. \end{cases}$$

Since these equations give $x + z = 0$, there is no way in which (x, y, z, w) can be written in terms of $(1, 2, -1, -1)$ and $(-1, 5, 1, 3)$ when $x + z \neq 0$, so this set of vectors does not span $\mathbb{R}^4$. So the set is not a basis for $\mathbb{R}^4$.

3.5 We check both conditions in Strategy 3.2.

First we use Strategy 3.1 for checking linear independence. Suppose that

$$\alpha \begin{pmatrix} 1 & 0 \\ 1 & 0 \end{pmatrix} + \beta \begin{pmatrix} 0 & -1 \\ 1 & 0 \end{pmatrix} + \gamma \begin{pmatrix} 2 & 0 \\ 0 & 1 \end{pmatrix}$$
$$+ \delta \begin{pmatrix} -3 & 1 \\ 0 & 0 \end{pmatrix} = \begin{pmatrix} 0 & 0 \\ 0 & 0 \end{pmatrix},$$

that is,

$$\begin{pmatrix} \alpha + 2\gamma - 3\delta & -\beta + \delta \\ \alpha + \beta & \gamma \end{pmatrix} = \begin{pmatrix} 0 & 0 \\ 0 & 0 \end{pmatrix}.$$

Equating corresponding entries, we see that α, β, γ and δ satisfy the simultaneous equations

$$\begin{cases} \alpha + 2\gamma - 3\delta = 0, \\ -\beta + \delta = 0, \\ \alpha + \beta = 0, \\ \gamma = 0. \end{cases}$$

From the fourth equation $\gamma = 0$, and adding the second equation to the third gives $\alpha + \delta = 0$. Substituting for γ in the first equation gives $\alpha - 3\delta = 0$. These last two equations give $\delta = 0$.

Then, by substitution, $\alpha = 0$ and $\beta = 0$, so the set S is linearly independent.

Next we check whether each 2×2 matrix can be written as a linear combination of the matrices in S.

Choosing $\begin{pmatrix} a & b \\ c & d \end{pmatrix}$ as an arbitrary 2×2 matrix, we seek numbers α, β, γ and δ such that

$$\begin{pmatrix} a & b \\ c & d \end{pmatrix} = \alpha \begin{pmatrix} 1 & 0 \\ 1 & 0 \end{pmatrix} + \beta \begin{pmatrix} 0 & -1 \\ 1 & 0 \end{pmatrix}$$
$$+ \gamma \begin{pmatrix} 2 & 0 \\ 0 & 1 \end{pmatrix} + \delta \begin{pmatrix} -3 & 1 \\ 0 & 0 \end{pmatrix}.$$

Equating corresponding entries, we see that α, β, γ and δ satisfy the simultaneous equations

$$\begin{cases} \alpha + 2\gamma - 3\delta = a, \\ -\beta + \delta = b, \\ \alpha + \beta = c, \\ \gamma = d. \end{cases}$$

From the fourth equation $\gamma = d$, and adding the second equation to the third gives $\alpha + \delta = b + c$. Substituting for γ in the first equation gives $\alpha - 3\delta = a - 2d$. These last two equations give $\delta = \frac{1}{4}(b + c - a + 2d)$.

Then, by substitution, $\alpha = \frac{1}{4}(a + 3b + 3c - 2d)$ and $\beta = \frac{1}{4}(-a - 3b + c + 2d)$. So the set of matrices S spans the set $M_{2,2}$ of all 2×2 matrices.

Thus S is a basis for $M_{2,2}$.

3.6 (a) $(2, 1)_E = 2(1, 2) + 1(-3, 1)$
$$= (2, 4) + (-3, 1)$$
$$= (-1, 5)$$

(b) $(1, 1, -1)_E = 1(1, 0, 2) + 1(-1, 1, 3) - 1(2, -2, 0)$
$$= (1, 0, 2) + (-1, 1, 3) - (2, -2, 0)$$
$$= (-2, 3, 5)$$

3.7 (a) We write

$$(5, -4) = \alpha(1, 2) + \beta(-3, 1).$$

This gives the simultaneous equations

$$\begin{cases} \alpha - 3\beta = 5, \\ 2\alpha + \beta = -4. \end{cases}$$

Solving these equations gives $\alpha = -1$, $\beta = -2$, so

$$(5, -4) = -1(1, 2) - 2(-3, 1)$$
$$= (-1, -2)_E.$$

(b) We write

$$(-3, 5, 7) = \alpha(1, 0, 2) + \beta(-1, 1, 3) + \gamma(2, -2, 0).$$

This gives the simultaneous equations

$$\begin{cases} \alpha - \beta + 2\gamma = -3, \\ \beta - 2\gamma = 5, \\ 2\alpha + 3\beta = 7. \end{cases}$$

Adding the first and second equations gives $\alpha = 2$, and substituting this into the third equation gives $\beta = 1$. Substituting for β in the second equation gives $\gamma = -2$.

So

$$(-3, 5, 7) = 2(1, 0, 2) + 1(-1, 1, 3) - 2(2, -2, 0)$$
$$= (2, 1, -2)_E.$$

3.8 (a) This set cannot be a basis for $\mathbb{R}^3$, as it contains only two vectors, not three.

(b) This set is linearly independent, as we showed in Exercise 3.3(b). It also contains three vectors, so it is a basis for $\mathbb{R}^3$.

(c) This set is not linearly independent, as

$$(1, -1, 0) + (2, 1, 4) = (3, 0, 4).$$

Therefore this set is not a basis for $\mathbb{R}^3$, although it contains the correct number of vectors.

(d) This set contains four vectors, so it cannot be a basis for $\mathbb{R}^3$.

3.9 (a) This set is not linearly independent, since it contains the zero vector.

(b) We use Strategy 3.1.

The equation

$$\alpha(1, 1, 0) + \beta(1, 0, 1) + \gamma(0, 1, 1) = (0, 0, 0)$$

simplifies to

$$(\alpha + \beta, \alpha + \gamma, \beta + \gamma) = (0, 0, 0).$$

Equating corresponding coordinates gives the simultaneous equations

$$\begin{cases} \alpha + \beta & = 0, \\ \alpha & + \gamma = 0, \\ \beta + \gamma = 0. \end{cases}$$

From the first equation $\alpha = -\beta$, and substituting this into the second gives $-\beta + \gamma = 0$. Adding this to the third equation gives $\gamma = 0$, and substitution into the other two equations gives $\alpha = \beta = 0$, so the set is linearly independent.

(c) Again we use Strategy 3.1.

The equation

$$\alpha(1 + 2x) + \beta(3x) + \gamma(2 - 4x) = 0 + 0x$$

simplifies to

$$1(\alpha + 2\gamma) + (2\alpha + 3\beta - 4\gamma)x = 0 + 0x.$$

Equating the coefficients of 1 and x gives

$$\begin{cases} \alpha & + 2\gamma = 0, \\ 2\alpha + 3\beta - 4\gamma = 0. \end{cases}$$

Choosing $\gamma = 1$, for example, gives the solution $\alpha = -2$, $\beta = \frac{8}{3}$ and $\gamma = 1$, so the set is not linearly independent.

3.10 (a) The set contains two vectors. They are linearly independent, as the second is not a multiple of the first. So S is a basis for $\mathbb{R}^2$, by Theorem 3.5.

(b) Two vectors cannot span $\mathbb{R}^3$, since $\mathbb{R}^3$ has dimension 3. Hence this is not a basis for $\mathbb{R}^3$.

(c) These vectors are linearly independent, since if

$$\alpha_1(1, 0, 0, 0) + \alpha_2(1, 1, 0, 0) + \alpha_3(1, 1, 1, 0)$$
$$+ \alpha_4(1, 1, 1, 1) = (0, 0, 0, 0),$$

then

$$\begin{cases} \alpha_1 + \alpha_2 + \alpha_3 + \alpha_4 = 0, \\ \alpha_2 + \alpha_3 + \alpha_4 = 0, \\ \alpha_3 + \alpha_4 = 0, \\ \alpha_4 = 0. \end{cases}$$

Solving these equations gives $\alpha_1 = \alpha_2 = \alpha_3 = \alpha_4 = 0$. So we have four linearly independent vectors, so S is a basis for $\mathbb{R}^4$, by Theorem 3.5.

3.11 (a) First we check for linear independence. If

$$\alpha \begin{pmatrix} 1 \\ 2 \end{pmatrix} + \beta \begin{pmatrix} 1 \\ 4 \end{pmatrix} = \begin{pmatrix} 0 \\ 0 \end{pmatrix},$$

then

$$\begin{cases} \alpha + \beta = 0, \\ 2\alpha + 4\beta = 0. \end{cases}$$

The only solution is $\alpha = \beta = 0$, so the set is linearly independent.

Second we check whether S spans $M_{2,1}$. For

$$\alpha \begin{pmatrix} 1 \\ 2 \end{pmatrix} + \beta \begin{pmatrix} 1 \\ 4 \end{pmatrix} = \begin{pmatrix} x \\ y \end{pmatrix},$$

we require

$$\begin{cases} \alpha + \beta = x, \\ 2\alpha + 4\beta = y. \end{cases}$$

These equations have solution $\alpha = (4x - y)/2$ and $\beta = (y - 2x)/2$, so this set spans $M_{2,1}$.

Hence this set is a basis for $M_{2,1}$.

(b) First we check for linear independence. If

$$\alpha(2 + x) + \beta(3 - x^2) = 0,$$

then equating coefficients of 1, x and x^2 gives

$$\begin{cases} 2\alpha + 3\beta = 0, \\ \alpha = 0, \\ - \beta = 0. \end{cases}$$

The last two equations give $\alpha = 0$, $\beta = 0$, so the set is linearly independent.

Second we check whether S spans P_3. Let $a + bx + cx^2$ with $a, b, c \in \mathbb{R}$ be a typical vector of P_3. For

$$\alpha(2 + x) + \beta(3 - x^2) = a + bx + cx^2,$$

then, equating coefficients of 1, x and x^2, we require

$$\begin{cases} 2\alpha + 3\beta = a, \\ \alpha = b, \\ - \beta = c. \end{cases}$$

Substituting $\alpha = b$, $\beta = -c$ into the first equation gives $2b - 3c = a$, so these equations have a solution only when a, b and c satisfy this relationship.

So a typical vector of P_3 cannot be expressed in terms of these two vectors, and thus they do not span P_3.

The set S is therefore not a basis for P_3.

(c) The second vector is a multiple of the first, so the set is linearly dependent.

We do not need to check spanning because if the set is linearly dependent, then it is not a basis.

3.12 (a) True, by statement (2) after the definition of linear dependence on page 25.

(b) False, since $\mathbb{R}^3$ has dimension 3, by Theorem 3.4.

(c) True, since any set of more than n vectors in $\mathbb{R}^n$ is linearly dependent, by Theorem 3.3.

(d) True, by definition of a basis on page 29.

(e) True, again by definition of a basis.

(f) False, since a set of vectors which spans $\mathbb{R}^n$ may contain more than n vectors, and hence is not linearly independent. (See Example 2.6(b).)

(g) False, since, for example, the set $\{(1,0)\}$ is linearly independent in $\mathbb{R}^2$, but does not span $\mathbb{R}^2$.

(h) True, by definition of a basis.

(i) False, since if any vector could be expressed in this way, then the set would be linearly dependent.

4.1 We use Strategy 4.1.

S contains the zero vector of $\mathbb{R}^2$: if $x = 0$, then $(x, -2x) = (0,0)$.

Let $\mathbf{v}_1 = (x_1, -2x_1)$ and $\mathbf{v}_2 = (x_2, -2x_2)$ belong to S. Then

$$\mathbf{v}_1 + \mathbf{v}_2 = (x_1, -2x_1) + (x_2, -2x_2)$$
$$= (x_1 + x_2, -2x_1 - 2x_2)$$
$$= (x_1 + x_2, -2(x_1 + x_2)).$$

This vector has the correct form for a vector in S, since $x_1 + x_2 \in \mathbb{R}$, so S is closed under vector addition.

Let $\mathbf{v} = (x, -2x) \in S$ and $\alpha \in \mathbb{R}$. Then

$$\alpha\mathbf{v} = \alpha(x, -2x) = (\alpha x, \alpha(-2x)) = (\alpha x, -2(\alpha x)).$$

This vector has the correct form for a vector in S, since $\alpha x \in \mathbb{R}$, so S is closed under scalar multiplication.

Thus S is a subspace of $\mathbb{R}^2$. (This subspace is the line through the origin with equation $y = -2x$.)

4.2 We use Strategy 4.1.

(a) If $\mathbf{0} \in S$, then $(x, x+2) = (0,0)$ for some number x; that is,

$$\begin{cases} x & = 0, \\ x + 2 = 0. \end{cases}$$

There is no value of x that simultaneously satisfies these two equations, so $\mathbf{0}$ does not belong to S.

So S is not a subspace of $\mathbb{R}^2$.

(b) S contains the zero vector of $\mathbb{R}^3$: choosing $y = z = 0$ gives $(0,0,0)$.

Let $\mathbf{v}_1 = (z_1 - y_1, y_1, z_1)$ and $\mathbf{v}_2 = (z_2 - y_2, y_2, z_2)$ belong to S. Then

$$\mathbf{v}_1 + \mathbf{v}_2$$
$$= (z_1 - y_1, y_1, z_1) + (z_2 - y_2, y_2, z_2)$$
$$= (z_1 - y_1 + z_2 - y_2, y_1 + y_2, z_1 + z_2)$$
$$= ((z_1 + z_2) - (y_1 + y_2), y_1 + y_2, z_1 + z_2).$$

This vector has the correct form for a vector in S, so S is closed under vector addition.

Let $\mathbf{v} = (z - y, y, z) \in S$ and $\alpha \in \mathbb{R}$. Then

$$\alpha\mathbf{v} = \alpha(z - y, y, z)$$
$$= (\alpha(z - y), \alpha y, \alpha z)$$
$$= (\alpha z - \alpha y, \alpha y, \alpha z).$$

This vector has the correct form for a vector in S, so S is closed under scalar multiplication.

So S is a subspace of $\mathbb{R}^3$. (It is the plane through the origin with equation $x + y - z = 0$.)

(c) S contains the zero vector of $\mathbb{R}^4$: choosing $x = y = z = 0$ gives $(0,0,0,0)$.

Let $\mathbf{v}_1 = (x_1, y_1, z_1, x_1 + 2y_1 - z_1)$ and $\mathbf{v}_2 = (x_2, y_2, z_2, x_2 + 2y_2 - z_2)$ belong to S. Then

$$\mathbf{v}_1 + \mathbf{v}_2 = (x_1, y_1, z_1, x_1 + 2y_1 - z_1)$$
$$+ (x_2, y_2, z_2, x_2 + 2y_2 - z_2)$$
$$= (x_1 + x_2, y_1 + y_2, z_1 + z_2,$$
$$x_1 + 2y_1 - z_1 + x_2 + 2y_2 - z_2)$$
$$= (x_1 + x_2, y_1 + y_2, z_1 + z_2,$$
$$(x_1 + x_2) + 2(y_1 + y_2) - (z_1 + z_2)).$$

This vector has the correct form for a vector in S, so S is closed under vector addition.

Let $\mathbf{v} = (x, y, z, x + 2y - z) \in S$ and $\alpha \in \mathbb{R}$. Then

$$\alpha\mathbf{v} = \alpha(x, y, z, x + 2y - z)$$
$$= (\alpha x, \alpha y, \alpha z, \alpha(x + 2y - z))$$
$$= (\alpha x, \alpha y, \alpha z, (\alpha x) + 2(\alpha y) - (\alpha z)).$$

This vector has the correct form for a vector in S, so S is closed under scalar multiplication.

So S is a subspace of $\mathbb{R}^4$; it is three-dimensional, so it is a hyperplane.

4.3 As before, we use Strategy 4.1.

(a) The set contains the zero vector, as $a = b = 0$ gives $p(x) = 0 + 0x = \mathbf{0}$.

Let $p_1(x) = a_1 + b_1 x$ and $p_2(x) = a_2 + b_2 x$. Then

$$p_1(x) + p_2(x) = a_1 + b_1 x + a_2 + b_2 x$$
$$= (a_1 + a_2) + (b_1 + b_2)x.$$

This polynomial has the correct form for a vector in S, so S is closed under vector addition.

Let $p(x) = a + bx$ and $\alpha \in \mathbb{R}$. Then

$$\alpha p(x) = \alpha a + \alpha bx = (\alpha a) + (\alpha b)x.$$

This polynomial has the correct form for a vector in S, so S is closed under scalar multiplication.

So S is a subspace of V.

(b) To show that a set is not a subspace, there is no need to check all the axioms in turn if it is likely that a later axiom will fail.

Let $p(x) = x + ax^2$ and $\alpha \in \mathbb{R}$. Then

$$\alpha p(x) = \alpha x + \alpha a x^2.$$

This vector does not have the correct form for a vector in S if $\alpha \neq 1$, so S is not closed under scalar multiplication.

So S is not a subspace of V.

(c) Let

$$\mathbf{A}_1 = \begin{pmatrix} a_1 & 1 \\ 0 & d_1 \end{pmatrix} \quad \text{and} \quad \mathbf{A}_2 = \begin{pmatrix} a_2 & 1 \\ 0 & d_2 \end{pmatrix}.$$

Then

$$\mathbf{A}_1 + \mathbf{A}_2 = \begin{pmatrix} a_1 & 1 \\ 0 & d_1 \end{pmatrix} + \begin{pmatrix} a_2 & 1 \\ 0 & d_2 \end{pmatrix}$$
$$= \begin{pmatrix} a_1 + a_2 & 2 \\ 0 & d_1 + d_2 \end{pmatrix}.$$

This matrix does not have the correct form for a vector in S, as can be seen from the top right-hand entry.

So S is not a subspace of V.

4.4 Since $\{(1, -2, 0), (0, 3, 3)\}$ is a linearly independent set, the subspace it spans is a two-dimensional subspace of $\mathbb{R}^3$, and is therefore a plane through the origin with equation

$$ax + by + cz = 0,$$

where a, b, c are not all zero.

Since the vectors in the spanning set lie in the plane, the values of a, b and c must satisfy the simultaneous equations

$$\begin{cases} a - 2b & = 0, \\ 3b + 3c & = 0. \end{cases}$$

The first of these equations gives $a = 2b$, and the second equation gives $c = -b$, so the subspace is the plane with equation $2bx + by - bz = 0$, or, equivalently,

$$2x + y - z = 0.$$

4.5 We use the form of the vectors in S to help us find a possible basis. Since

$$(x, y, z, x + 2y - z)$$
$$= x(1, 0, 0, 1) + y(0, 1, 0, 2) + z(0, 0, 1, -1),$$

any vector in S can be written as a linear combination of the vectors in the set

$$\{(1, 0, 0, 1), (0, 1, 0, 2), (0, 0, 1, -1)\},$$

so this set spans S.

The vectors in the set are also linearly independent, which can be checked by writing down the linear combination

$$\alpha(1, 0, 0, 1) + \beta(0, 1, 0, 2) + \gamma(0, 0, 1, -1)$$
$$= (0, 0, 0, 0)$$

and solving the resulting simultaneous equations

$$\begin{cases} \alpha & = 0, \\ \beta & = 0, \\ \gamma & = 0, \\ \alpha + 2\beta - \gamma & = 0, \end{cases}$$

to obtain $\alpha = \beta = \gamma = 0$.

So $\{(1, 0, 0, 1), (0, 1, 0, 2), (0, 0, 1, -1)\}$ is a basis for S. Therefore S has dimension 3. (It is a hyperplane in $\mathbb{R}^4$.)

4.6 Let the vector space be V and the subset S, and suppose that conditions (a), (b) and (c) of Theorem 4.1 hold.

We consider the axioms in turn.

A1 This holds for S, by condition (b).

A2 This holds for S, by condition (a).

A3 If $\mathbf{v} \in S$, then $-\mathbf{v}$ is also in S, by condition (c). Therefore each vector in S also has an inverse in S, so the axiom holds.

A4 This holds because if

$$(\mathbf{v} + \mathbf{w}) + \mathbf{z} = \mathbf{v} + (\mathbf{w} + \mathbf{z})$$

for all $\mathbf{v}$, $\mathbf{w}$ and $\mathbf{z}$ in V, then it also holds for all vectors in S, since S is a subset of V and therefore each vector in S is also in V.

A5 This holds for the same reason as A4; namely, if it holds for V, then it also holds for S, since each vector in S is also in V.

S1 This holds, by condition (c).

S2 This holds because it holds for all vectors in V, and each vector in S is also in V.

S3 Again, this holds because it holds for all vectors in V, and therefore for all vectors in S.

D1 and D2 These both hold for all vectors in V, and therefore also hold for all vectors in S, since S is a subset of V.

Since all the axioms hold for S if the conditions of Theorem 4.1 hold, S is a subspace of V.

4.7 (a) S contains the zero vector: choosing $x = y = 0$ gives $(0, 0, 0)$.

Let $\mathbf{v} = (x_1, y_1, 2x_1 + y_1)$ and $\mathbf{w} = (x_2, y_2, 2x_2 + y_2)$ belong to S. Then

$$\mathbf{v} + \mathbf{w} = (x_1, y_1, 2x_1 + y_1) + (x_2, y_2, 2x_2 + y_2)$$
$$= (x_1 + x_2, y_1 + y_2, 2(x_1 + x_2) + (y_1 + y_2)).$$

This vector has the correct form for a vector in S, so S is closed under vector addition.

Let $\mathbf{v} = (x, y, 2x + y) \in S$ and $\alpha \in \mathbb{R}$. Then
$$\alpha\mathbf{v} = \alpha(x, y, 2x + y)$$
$$= (\alpha x, \alpha y, 2(\alpha x) + (\alpha y)).$$
This vector has the correct form for a vector in S, so S is closed under scalar multiplication.

So S is a subspace of $\mathbb{R}^3$. (It is the plane through the origin with equation $2x + y - z = 0$.)

(b) S does not contain the zero vector because there is no value of x for which $(x, x - 3) = (0, 0)$.

So S is not a subspace of $\mathbb{R}^2$.

(c) S contains the zero vector: choosing $x = y = 0$ gives $(0, 0, 0, 0)$.

Let $\mathbf{v} = (x_1, y_1, x_1 - 3y_1, 2x_1 + y_1)$ and $\mathbf{w} = (x_2, y_2, x_2 - 3y_2, 2x_2 + y_2)$ belong to S. Then
$$\mathbf{v} + \mathbf{w} = (x_1, y_1, x_1 - 3y_1, 2x_1 + y_1)$$
$$+ (x_2, y_2, x_2 - 3y_2, 2x_2 + y_2)$$
$$= (x_1 + x_2, y_1 + y_2, (x_1 + x_2) - 3(y_1 + y_2),$$
$$2(x_1 + x_2) + (y_1 + y_2)).$$
This vector has the correct form for a vector in S, so S is closed under vector addition.

Let $\mathbf{v} = (x, y, x - 3y, 2x + y) \in S$ and $\alpha \in \mathbb{R}$. Then
$$\alpha\mathbf{v} = \alpha(x, y, x - 3y, 2x + y)$$
$$= (\alpha x, \alpha y, (\alpha x) - 3(\alpha y), 2(\alpha x) + (\alpha y)).$$
This vector has the correct form for a vector in S, so S is closed under scalar multiplication.

So S is a subspace of $\mathbb{R}^4$.

(d) S contains the zero vector: choosing $a = 0$ gives $0x^2 = \mathbf{0}$.

Let $\mathbf{v} = a_1 x^2$ and $\mathbf{w} = a_2 x^2$ belong to S. Then
$$\mathbf{v} + \mathbf{w} = a_1 x^2 + a_2 x^2 = (a_1 + a_2)x^2.$$
This vector has the correct form for a vector in S, so S is closed under vector addition.

Let $\mathbf{v} = ax^2 \in S$ and $\alpha \in \mathbb{R}$. Then
$$\alpha\mathbf{v} = \alpha(ax^2) = (\alpha a)x^2.$$
This vector has the correct form for a vector in S, so S is closed under scalar multiplication.

So S is a subspace of P_3.

(e) S is a subspace, by Theorem 4.2.

(f) S is not closed under scalar multiplication because if we choose $\alpha = -2$ and (x, y) in S with $x > 0$, then
$$\alpha(x, y) = -2(x, y) = (-2x, -2y).$$
Since $x > 0$, $-2x < 0$, so this vector is not in S.

So S is not a subspace of $\mathbb{R}^2$.

4.8 (a) Any vector in S can be written as
$$(x, y, 2x + y) = x(1, 0, 2) + y(0, 1, 1).$$
So $\{(1, 0, 2), (0, 1, 1)\}$ spans S.

Since this set is linearly independent (the two vectors are not multiples of each other), it is a basis for the subspace, which therefore has dimension 2.

(b) This is not a subspace.

(c) Any vector in S can be written as
$$(x, y, x - 3y, 2x + y)$$
$$= x(1, 0, 1, 2) + y(0, 1, -3, 1).$$
So $\{(1, 0, 1, 2), (0, 1, -3, 1)\}$ spans S. Since this set is linearly independent (the two vectors are not multiples of each other), it is a basis for the subspace, which therefore has dimension 2.

(d) Any vector in S is of the form ax^2, so it is a multiple of the vector x^2. Therefore $\{x^2\}$ spans S. Since this set is linearly independent, it is a basis for S, which therefore has dimension 1.

(e) $\left\{ \begin{pmatrix} 1 \\ 0 \\ 3 \end{pmatrix}, \begin{pmatrix} -1 \\ 2 \\ 0 \end{pmatrix} \right\}$ spans S, since S is defined as the span of this set of vectors.

Since these matrices are not multiples of each other, they are linearly independent. So this set is a basis for S, which therefore has dimension 2.

(f) This is not a subspace.

5.1 $\mathbf{v}_1 \cdot \mathbf{v}_2 = ((-2) \times 9) + (6 \times 3) = 0$,
so $\mathbf{v}_1$ and $\mathbf{v}_2$ are orthogonal.
$$\mathbf{v}_1 \cdot \mathbf{v}_3 = ((-2) \times 5) + (6 \times (-15)) = -100,$$
which is non-zero, so $\mathbf{v}_1$ and $\mathbf{v}_3$ are not orthogonal.
$$\mathbf{v}_2 \cdot \mathbf{v}_3 = (9 \times 5) + (3 \times (-15)) = 0,$$
so $\mathbf{v}_2$ and $\mathbf{v}_3$ are orthogonal.

5.2 (a) Let $\mathbf{v}_1 = (3, 4, 0)$, $\mathbf{v}_2 = (8, -6, 0)$ and $\mathbf{v}_3 = (0, 0, 5)$. Then
$$\mathbf{v}_1 \cdot \mathbf{v}_2 = (3 \times 8) + (4 \times (-6)) + (0 \times 0) = 0,$$
$$\mathbf{v}_1 \cdot \mathbf{v}_3 = (3 \times 0) + (4 \times 0) + (0 \times 5) = 0,$$
$$\mathbf{v}_2 \cdot \mathbf{v}_3 = (8 \times 0) + ((-6) \times 0) + (0 \times 5) = 0.$$
Thus $\{\mathbf{v}_1, \mathbf{v}_2, \mathbf{v}_3\}$ is an orthogonal set in $\mathbb{R}^3$. Since there are three vectors in this set, it is an orthogonal basis for $\mathbb{R}^3$.

(b) Let $(10, 0, 4)$
$$= \alpha_1(3, 4, 0) + \alpha_2(8, -6, 0) + \alpha_3(0, 0, 5). \qquad \text{(S.1)}$$
Forming the dot product of equation (S.1) with $(3, 4, 0)$, we obtain
$$(3, 4, 0) \cdot (10, 0, 4) = \alpha_1(3, 4, 0) \cdot (3, 4, 0),$$
that is, $30 = 25\alpha_1$, so $\alpha_1 = \frac{6}{5}$.

Forming the dot product of equation (S.1) with $(8, -6, 0)$, we obtain
$$(8, -6, 0) \cdot (10, 0, 4) = \alpha_2(8, -6, 0) \cdot (8, -6, 0),$$
that is, $80 = 100\alpha_2$, so $\alpha_2 = \frac{4}{5}$.

Forming the dot product of equation (S.1) with $(0, 0, 5)$, we obtain

$$(0, 0, 5) \cdot (10, 0, 4) = \alpha_3 (0, 0, 5) \cdot (0, 0, 5),$$

that is, $20 = 25\alpha_3$, so $\alpha_3 = \frac{4}{5}$.

(Alternatively, α_1, α_2 and α_3 can be obtained from the formula in Frame 6.)

Thus

$$(10, 0, 4) = \tfrac{6}{5}(3, 4, 0) + \tfrac{4}{5}(8, -6, 0) + \tfrac{4}{5}(0, 0, 5).$$

5.3 We follow Strategy 5.1 in Frame 8.

The plane through the origin orthogonal to $(3, -4, 5)$ has equation $3x - 4y + 5z = 0$.

Method 1 (Frame 9)   Let $\mathbf{v}_1$ be any non-zero vector in this plane—for example, $\mathbf{v}_1 = (4, 3, 0)$.

Let $\mathbf{v}_2 = (x, y, z)$ be any non-zero vector orthogonal to $\mathbf{v}_1$ in the plane. Then

$$4x + 3y = 0 \quad \text{and} \quad 3x - 4y + 5z = 0;$$

thus $x = -\frac{3}{4}y$ and $z = \frac{5}{4}y$.

So any non-zero vector of the form $\left(-\frac{3}{4}y, y, \frac{5}{4}y\right)$ can be taken for $\mathbf{v}_2$—for example, $\mathbf{v}_2 = (-3, 4, 5)$.

So an orthogonal basis for $\mathbb{R}^3$ is

$$\{(3, -4, 5), (4, 3, 0), (-3, 4, 5)\}.$$

Method 2 (Frame 10)   We choose a basis for the plane—for example, $\{(4, 3, 0), (0, 5, 4)\}$.

Let $\mathbf{v}_1 = (4, 3, 0)$ and $\mathbf{v}_2 = (0, 5, 4) - \alpha\mathbf{v}_1$, where α is chosen so that $\mathbf{v}_1 \cdot \mathbf{v}_2 = 0$. Then

$$\mathbf{v}_1 \cdot \mathbf{v}_2 = (4, 3, 0) \cdot (0, 5, 4) - \alpha(4, 3, 0) \cdot (4, 3, 0) = 0,$$

which gives $15 = 25\alpha$, so $\alpha = \frac{3}{5}$ and

$$\mathbf{v}_2 = (0, 5, 4) - \tfrac{3}{5}(4, 3, 0) = \left(-\tfrac{12}{5}, \tfrac{16}{5}, 4\right).$$

So an orthogonal basis for $\mathbb{R}^3$ is

$$\left\{(3, -4, 5), (4, 3, 0), \left(-\tfrac{12}{5}, \tfrac{16}{5}, 4\right)\right\}.$$

(Note that if you choose a different basis for the plane, then you obtain a different orthogonal basis.)

5.4 (a) $(1, 2, -1, 0) \cdot (0, -5, 6, -3)$
$$= (1 \times 0) + (2 \times (-5)) + ((-1) \times 6) + (0 \times (-3))$$
$$= 0 - 10 - 6 + 0 = -16$$

(b) $1, 2, 3, 4, 5, 6) \cdot (3, 2, 1, 0, -1, -2)$
$$= (1 \times 3) + (2 \times 2) + (3 \times 1) + (4 \times 0)$$
$$\quad + (5 \times (-1)) + (6 \times (-2))$$
$$= 3 + 4 + 3 + 0 - 5 - 12 = -7$$

5.5 We form the dot product of each pair of vectors in the set:

$$(1, 2, 1, 0) \cdot (-1, 1, -1, 1) = -1 + 2 - 1 + 0 = 0,$$
$$(1, 2, 1, 0) \cdot (1, 0, -1, 0) = 1 + 0 - 1 + 0 = 0,$$
$$(1, 2, 1, 0) \cdot (1, -1, 1, 3) = 1 - 2 + 1 + 0 = 0,$$
$$(-1, 1, -1, 1) \cdot (1, 0, -1, 0) = -1 + 0 + 1 + 0 = 0,$$
$$(-1, 1, -1, 1) \cdot (1, -1, 1, 3) = -1 - 1 - 1 + 3 = 0,$$
$$(1, 0, -1, 0) \cdot (1, -1, 1, 3) = 1 + 0 - 1 + 0 = 0.$$

So these vectors form an orthogonal basis for $\mathbb{R}^4$.

5.6 We use Strategy 5.3.

Let $\mathbf{v}_1 = (1, 2, 1, 0)$, $\mathbf{v}_2 = (-1, 1, -1, 1)$, $\mathbf{v}_3 = (1, 0, -1, 0)$, $\mathbf{v}_4 = (1, -1, 1, 3)$ and $\mathbf{u} = (1, 2, 3, 4)$. Then

$$\alpha_1 = \frac{(1, 2, 1, 0) \cdot (1, 2, 3, 4)}{(1, 2, 1, 0) \cdot (1, 2, 1, 0)} = \frac{8}{6} = \frac{4}{3},$$

$$\alpha_2 = \frac{(-1, 1, -1, 1) \cdot (1, 2, 3, 4)}{(-1, 1, -1, 1) \cdot (-1, 1, -1, 1)} = \frac{2}{4} = \frac{1}{2},$$

$$\alpha_3 = \frac{(1, 0, -1, 0) \cdot (1, 2, 3, 4)}{(1, 0, -1, 0) \cdot (1, 0, -1, 0)} = \frac{-2}{2} = -1,$$

$$\alpha_4 = \frac{(1, -1, 1, 3) \cdot (1, 2, 3, 4)}{(1, -1, 1, 3) \cdot (1, -1, 1, 3)} = \frac{14}{12} = \frac{7}{6}.$$

Thus

$$(1, 2, 3, 4) = \tfrac{4}{3}(1, 2, 1, 0) + \tfrac{1}{2}(-1, 1, -1, 1)$$
$$- (1, 0, -1, 0) + \tfrac{7}{6}(1, -1, 1, 3).$$

5.7 We apply Theorem 5.4 with $\mathbf{w}_1 = (1, 2, 1, 0, 0)$, $\mathbf{w}_2 = (-1, 1, -1, 1, 0)$, $\mathbf{w}_3 = (0, 0, 0, 0, 1)$, $\mathbf{w}_4 = (1, 0, 0, 0, 0)$ and $\mathbf{w}_5 = (0, 1, 0, 0, 0)$.

Since $\mathbf{w}_1$, $\mathbf{w}_2$ and $\mathbf{w}_3$ already form an orthogonal set, we have

$$\mathbf{v}_1 = \mathbf{w}_1 = (1, 2, 1, 0, 0),$$
$$\mathbf{v}_2 = \mathbf{w}_2 = (-1, 1, -1, 1, 0)$$

and

$$\mathbf{v}_3 = \mathbf{w}_3 = (0, 0, 0, 0, 1).$$

Then

$$\mathbf{v}_4 = \mathbf{w}_4 - \left(\frac{\mathbf{v}_1 \cdot \mathbf{w}_4}{\mathbf{v}_1 \cdot \mathbf{v}_1}\right)\mathbf{v}_1 - \left(\frac{\mathbf{v}_2 \cdot \mathbf{w}_4}{\mathbf{v}_2 \cdot \mathbf{v}_2}\right)\mathbf{v}_2$$
$$- \left(\frac{\mathbf{v}_3 \cdot \mathbf{w}_4}{\mathbf{v}_3 \cdot \mathbf{v}_3}\right)\mathbf{v}_3$$
$$= (1, 0, 0, 0, 0) - \tfrac{1}{6}(1, 2, 1, 0, 0)$$
$$+ \tfrac{1}{4}(-1, 1, -1, 1, 0) - 0$$
$$= \left(\tfrac{7}{12}, -\tfrac{1}{12}, -\tfrac{5}{12}, \tfrac{1}{4}, 0\right)$$

and

$$\mathbf{v}_5 = \mathbf{w}_5 - \left(\frac{\mathbf{v}_1 \cdot \mathbf{w}_5}{\mathbf{v}_1 \cdot \mathbf{v}_1}\right)\mathbf{v}_1 - \left(\frac{\mathbf{v}_2 \cdot \mathbf{w}_5}{\mathbf{v}_2 \cdot \mathbf{v}_2}\right)\mathbf{v}_2$$
$$- \left(\frac{\mathbf{v}_3 \cdot \mathbf{w}_5}{\mathbf{v}_3 \cdot \mathbf{v}_3}\right)\mathbf{v}_3 - \left(\frac{\mathbf{v}_4 \cdot \mathbf{w}_5}{\mathbf{v}_4 \cdot \mathbf{v}_4}\right)\mathbf{v}_4$$
$$= (0, 1, 0, 0, 0) - \tfrac{1}{3}(1, 2, 1, 0, 0) - \tfrac{1}{4}(-1, 1, -1, 1, 0)$$
$$- 0 + \tfrac{1}{7}\left(\tfrac{7}{12}, -\tfrac{1}{12}, -\tfrac{5}{12}, \tfrac{1}{4}, 0\right)$$
$$= \left(0, \tfrac{3}{42}, -\tfrac{3}{21}, -\tfrac{9}{42}, 0\right) = \left(0, \tfrac{1}{14}, -\tfrac{1}{7}, -\tfrac{3}{14}, 0\right).$$

Thus we have the orthogonal basis

$$\{(1, 2, 1, 0, 0), (-1, 1, -1, 1, 0), (0, 0, 0, 0, 1),$$
$$\left(\tfrac{7}{12}, -\tfrac{1}{12}, -\tfrac{5}{12}, \tfrac{1}{4}, 0\right), \left(0, \tfrac{1}{14}, -\tfrac{1}{7}, -\tfrac{3}{14}, 0\right)\}.$$

5.8 (a) $(3, -4, 5) \cdot (3, -4, 5) = 9 + 16 + 25 = 50$,

so $\|(3, -4, 5)\| = \sqrt{50} = 5\sqrt{2}$.

(b) $(1, 2, -1, 0, 3) \cdot (1, 2, -1, 0, 3)$
$$= 1 + 4 + 1 + 0 + 9 = 15,$$

so $\|(1, 2, -1, 0, 3)\| = \sqrt{15}$.

5.9 If $\mathbf{v} = (v_1, v_2, \ldots, v_n)$ is a non-zero vector, then

$$\frac{\mathbf{v}}{\|\mathbf{v}\|} = \left(\frac{v_1}{\sqrt{\mathbf{v} \cdot \mathbf{v}}}, \frac{v_2}{\sqrt{\mathbf{v} \cdot \mathbf{v}}}, \ldots, \frac{v_n}{\sqrt{\mathbf{v} \cdot \mathbf{v}}} \right),$$

so the length of $\mathbf{v}/\|\mathbf{v}\|$ is

$$\sqrt{\frac{v_1^2}{\mathbf{v} \cdot \mathbf{v}} + \frac{v_2^2}{\mathbf{v} \cdot \mathbf{v}} + \cdots + \frac{v_n^2}{\mathbf{v} \cdot \mathbf{v}}}$$

$$= \sqrt{\frac{v_1^2 + v_2^2 + \cdots + v_n^2}{\mathbf{v} \cdot \mathbf{v}}}$$

$$= \sqrt{\frac{\mathbf{v} \cdot \mathbf{v}}{\mathbf{v} \cdot \mathbf{v}}} = 1.$$

5.10 We use Strategy 5.4.

Since $\|(1, 2, 1, 0)\| = \sqrt{6}$, $\|(-1, 1, -1, 1)\| = \sqrt{4} = 2$, $\|(1, 0, -1, 0)\| = \sqrt{2}$ and $\|(1, -1, 1, 3)\| = \sqrt{12} = 2\sqrt{3}$, the required orthonormal basis for $\mathbb{R}^4$ is

$$\left\{ \left(\frac{1}{\sqrt{6}}, \frac{2}{\sqrt{6}}, \frac{1}{\sqrt{6}}, 0 \right), \left(-\frac{1}{2}, \frac{1}{2}, -\frac{1}{2}, \frac{1}{2} \right), \right.$$
$$\left. \left(\frac{1}{\sqrt{2}}, 0, -\frac{1}{\sqrt{2}}, 0 \right), \left(\frac{1}{2\sqrt{3}}, -\frac{1}{2\sqrt{3}}, \frac{1}{2\sqrt{3}}, \frac{3}{2\sqrt{3}} \right) \right\}.$$

5.11 (a) $\mathbf{v}_1 \cdot \mathbf{v}_2 = (1 \times 2) + (5 \times 8) + ((-3) \times 0)$
$$+ (4 \times (-7)) + ((-7) \times (-2))$$
$$= 2 + 40 + 0 - 28 + 14 = 28$$

(b) $\mathbf{v}_1 \cdot \mathbf{v}_1 = 1^2 + 5^2 + (-3)^2 + 4^2 + (-7)^2$
$$= 1 + 25 + 9 + 16 + 49 = 100,$$

so the length of $\mathbf{v}_1$ is $\sqrt{100} = 10$.

$$\mathbf{v}_2 \cdot \mathbf{v}_2 = 2^2 + 8^2 + 0^2 + (-7)^2 + (-2)^2$$
$$= 4 + 64 + 0 + 49 + 4 = 121,$$

so the length of $\mathbf{v}_2$ is $\sqrt{121} = 11$.

5.12 (a) We have

$(5, 5, 5, 5) \cdot (5, -5, -5, 5) = 25 - 25 - 25 + 25 = 0$,
$(5, 5, 5, 5) \cdot (5, 0, 0, -5) = 25 + 0 + 0 - 25 = 0$,
$(5, 5, 5, 5) \cdot (0, 5, -5, 0) = 0 + 25 - 25 + 0 = 0$,
$(5, -5, -5, 5) \cdot (5, 0, 0, -5) = 25 + 0 + 0 - 25 = 0$,
$(5, -5, -5, 5) \cdot (0, 5, -5, 0) = 0 - 25 + 25 + 0 = 0$,
$(5, 0, 0, -5) \cdot (0, 5, -5, 0) = 0 + 0 + 0 + 0 = 0$.

Thus the given vectors form an orthogonal set. Since there are four of them, they form an orthogonal basis for $\mathbb{R}^4$.

(b) By Theorem 5.3,

$$(5, 0, 0, 0) = \tfrac{25}{100}(5, 5, 5, 5) + \tfrac{25}{100}(5, -5, -5, 5)$$
$$+ \tfrac{25}{50}(5, 0, 0, -5) + \tfrac{0}{50}(0, 5, -5, 0)$$
$$= \tfrac{1}{4}(5, 5, 5, 5) + \tfrac{1}{4}(5, -5, -5, 5)$$
$$+ \tfrac{1}{2}(5, 0, 0, -5) + 0(0, 5, -5, 0).$$

(c) $\|(5, 5, 5, 5)\| = \sqrt{5^2 + 5^2 + 5^2 + 5^2} = \sqrt{100} = 10$,

$\|(5, -5, -5, 5)\| = \sqrt{5^2 + (-5)^2 + (-5)^2 + 5^2}$
$$= \sqrt{100} = 10,$$

$\|(5, 0, 0, -5)\| = \sqrt{5^2 + 0^2 + 0^2 + (-5)^2}$
$$= \sqrt{50} = 5\sqrt{2},$$

$\|(0, 5, -5, 0)\| = \sqrt{0^2 + 5^2 + (-5)^2 + 0^2}$
$$= \sqrt{50} = 5\sqrt{2}.$$

Thus the corresponding orthonormal basis for $\mathbb{R}^4$ is

$$\left\{ \left(\frac{1}{2}, \frac{1}{2}, \frac{1}{2}, \frac{1}{2} \right), \left(\frac{1}{2}, -\frac{1}{2}, -\frac{1}{2}, \frac{1}{2} \right), \right.$$
$$\left. \left(\frac{1}{\sqrt{2}}, 0, 0, -\frac{1}{\sqrt{2}} \right), \left(0, \frac{1}{\sqrt{2}}, -\frac{1}{\sqrt{2}}, 0 \right) \right\}.$$

5.13 (a) We first choose a basis for $\mathbb{R}^3$ containing the vector $(1, -2, 2)$—say $\mathbf{w}_1 = (1, -2, 2)$, $\mathbf{w}_2 = (1, 0, 0)$ and $\mathbf{w}_3 = (0, 1, 0)$.

Let $\mathbf{v}_1 = \mathbf{w}_1 = (1, -2, 2)$,

$$\mathbf{v}_2 = \mathbf{w}_2 - \left(\frac{\mathbf{v}_1 \cdot \mathbf{w}_2}{\mathbf{v}_1 \cdot \mathbf{v}_1} \right) \mathbf{v}_1$$
$$= (1, 0, 0) - \tfrac{1}{9}(1, -2, 2) = \left(\tfrac{8}{9}, \tfrac{2}{9}, -\tfrac{2}{9} \right)$$

and

$$\mathbf{v}_3 = \mathbf{w}_3 - \left(\frac{\mathbf{v}_1 \cdot \mathbf{w}_3}{\mathbf{v}_1 \cdot \mathbf{v}_1} \right) \mathbf{v}_1 - \left(\frac{\mathbf{v}_2 \cdot \mathbf{w}_3}{\mathbf{v}_2 \cdot \mathbf{v}_2} \right) \mathbf{v}_2$$
$$= (0, 1, 0) + \tfrac{2}{9}(1, -2, 2) - \tfrac{1}{4} \left(\tfrac{8}{9}, \tfrac{2}{9}, -\tfrac{2}{9} \right)$$
$$= \left(0, \tfrac{1}{2}, \tfrac{1}{2} \right).$$

The required basis for $\mathbb{R}^3$ is therefore

$$\left\{ (1, -2, 2), \left(\tfrac{8}{9}, \tfrac{2}{9}, -\tfrac{2}{9} \right), \left(0, \tfrac{1}{2}, \tfrac{1}{2} \right) \right\}.$$

(b) We first calculate the length of each basis vector:

$$\|(1, -2, 2)\| = \sqrt{1^2 + (-2)^2 + 2^2} = \sqrt{9} = 3,$$

$$\left\| \left(\tfrac{8}{9}, \tfrac{2}{9}, -\tfrac{2}{9} \right) \right\| = \sqrt{\left(\tfrac{8}{9} \right)^2 + \left(\tfrac{2}{9} \right)^2 + \left(-\tfrac{2}{9} \right)^2}$$
$$= \sqrt{\tfrac{8}{9}} = \tfrac{2}{3}\sqrt{2}$$

and

$$\left\| \left(0, \tfrac{1}{2}, \tfrac{1}{2} \right) \right\| = \sqrt{0^2 + \left(\tfrac{1}{2} \right)^2 + \left(\tfrac{1}{2} \right)^2}$$
$$= \sqrt{\tfrac{1}{2}} = \tfrac{1}{2}\sqrt{2}.$$

Dividing each basis vector by its length, we obtain the orthonormal basis for $\mathbb{R}^3$

$$\left\{ \left(\tfrac{1}{3}, -\tfrac{2}{3}, \tfrac{2}{3} \right), \left(\tfrac{2}{3}\sqrt{2}, \tfrac{1}{6}\sqrt{2}, -\tfrac{1}{6}\sqrt{2} \right), \right.$$
$$\left. \left(0, \tfrac{1}{2}\sqrt{2}, \tfrac{1}{2}\sqrt{2} \right) \right\}.$$

5.14 The hyperplane $2x + 2y + z = 0$ consists of all the points of $\mathbb{R}^4$ which are orthogonal to the vector $(2, 2, 1, 0)$.

Let $\mathbf{w}_1 = (2, 2, 1, 0)$, $\mathbf{w}_2 = (1, 2, 0, 2)$, $\mathbf{w}_3 = (0, 1, 2, 2)$ and $\mathbf{w}_4 = (2, 0, 2, 1)$; then we use the Gram–Schmidt orthogonalisation process.

Let $\mathbf{v}_1 = \mathbf{w}_1 = (2, 2, 1, 0)$,

$$
\begin{aligned}
\mathbf{v}_2 &= \mathbf{w}_2 - \left(\frac{\mathbf{v}_1 \cdot \mathbf{w}_2}{\mathbf{v}_1 \cdot \mathbf{v}_1} \right) \mathbf{v}_1 \\
&= (1, 2, 0, 2) - \tfrac{2}{3}(2, 2, 1, 0) \\
&= \left(-\tfrac{1}{3}, \tfrac{2}{3}, -\tfrac{2}{3}, 2 \right),
\end{aligned}
$$

$$
\begin{aligned}
\mathbf{v}_3 &= \mathbf{w}_3 - \left(\frac{\mathbf{v}_1 \cdot \mathbf{w}_3}{\mathbf{v}_1 \cdot \mathbf{v}_1} \right) \mathbf{v}_1 - \left(\frac{\mathbf{v}_2 \cdot \mathbf{w}_3}{\mathbf{v}_2 \cdot \mathbf{v}_2} \right) \mathbf{v}_2 \\
&= (0, 1, 2, 2) - \tfrac{4}{9}(2, 2, 1, 0) - \tfrac{2}{3} \left(-\tfrac{1}{3}, \tfrac{2}{3}, -\tfrac{2}{3}, 2 \right) \\
&= \left(-\tfrac{2}{3}, -\tfrac{1}{3}, 2, \tfrac{2}{3} \right)
\end{aligned}
$$

and

$$
\begin{aligned}
\mathbf{v}_4 &= \mathbf{w}_4 - \left(\frac{\mathbf{v}_1 \cdot \mathbf{w}_4}{\mathbf{v}_1 \cdot \mathbf{v}_1} \right) \mathbf{v}_1 - \left(\frac{\mathbf{v}_2 \cdot \mathbf{w}_4}{\mathbf{v}_2 \cdot \mathbf{v}_2} \right) \mathbf{v}_2 \\
&\quad - \left(\frac{\mathbf{v}_3 \cdot \mathbf{w}_4}{\mathbf{v}_3 \cdot \mathbf{v}_3} \right) \mathbf{v}_3 \\
&= (2, 0, 2, 1) - \tfrac{2}{3}(2, 2, 1, 0) - 0 \left(-\tfrac{1}{3}, \tfrac{2}{3}, -\tfrac{2}{3}, 2 \right) \\
&\quad - \tfrac{2}{3} \left(-\tfrac{2}{3}, -\tfrac{1}{3}, 2, \tfrac{2}{3} \right) \\
&= \left(\tfrac{10}{9}, -\tfrac{10}{9}, 0, \tfrac{5}{9} \right).
\end{aligned}
$$

Thus an orthogonal basis for the hyperplane is

$$
\left\{ \left(-\tfrac{1}{3}, \tfrac{2}{3}, -\tfrac{2}{3}, 2 \right), \left(-\tfrac{2}{3}, -\tfrac{1}{3}, 2, \tfrac{2}{3} \right), \left(\tfrac{10}{9}, -\tfrac{10}{9}, 0, \tfrac{5}{9} \right) \right\}.
$$

Index